Overcoming Depression

A Cognitive Therapy Approach for Taming the Depression BEAST

Client Workbook

Mark Gilson
Arthur Freeman

Printed in the United States of America

1 2 3 4 5 6 7 8 9 10 11 12 A B C D E

Contents

Figures

Comments About the Program

This new patient treatment manual sets a high mark for presenting therapy in a clear and accessible manner to patients. It contains the fundamentals of treatment and self-help for the depressed individual in a readable and engaging format. The concept of BEAST (Body, Emotion, Action, Situation, and Thoughts) allows for an easy conceptualization of the components of mood and at the same time is whimsical and intriguing. It strikes just the right balance, and I believe it is a refined contribution to the psychotherapist's tool kit for providing empirically-supported treatment that helps people improve their mood and function better in their lives.

Aaron T. Beck, M.D.
President
The Beck Institute for Cognitive Therapy and Research
Bala Cynwyd, Pennsylvania

Overcoming Depression is a remarkably fine workbook for almost anyone suffering from sporadic or chronic depression. It succinctly and clearly provides many cognitive-behavioral methods that people experiencing depression can promptly put to good use. I highly recommend it.

Albert Ellis, Ph.D.
President
Albert Ellis Institute
New York, New York
Author of *A Guide to Rational Living*

Gilson and Freeman's *Overcoming Depression,* a client workbook, will be an important addition to the field. Easily readable, it communicates complex concepts in an understandable manner, and the take-home message—that depression is a treatable illness—comes through clearly. It provides accurate information to clients about both cognitive therapy and antidepressant medications. There is no doubt that this manual will be helpful to many clients and their families.

Charles B. Nemeroff, M.D., Ph.D.
Reunette W. Harris Professor and Chairman
Department of Psychiatry and Behavioral Sciences
Emory University School of Medicine
Atlanta, Georgia

About the Authors

Mark Gilson received his PhD in 1983 from Georgia State University. He is a fellow of the Academy of Clinical Psychology, American Board of Professional Psychology. Dr. Gilson was a postdoctoral fellow at the world-renowned Center for Cognitive Therapy at the University of Pennsylvania, where he studied with Aaron T. Beck, MD. He was later a faculty member in the Department of Psychiatry at the University of Pennsylvania. Dr. Gilson then moved to Atlanta and founded the Atlanta Center for Cognitive Therapy (ACCT). He has directed the training and certification program at ACCT for the past 14 years. For more information, see www.cognitiveatlanta.com. Dr. Gilson is an adjunct faculty member with both the Emory University Department of Psychiatry and the Georgia State University Department of Psychology. In November 1996, he was appointed coordinator of academic and professional issues for the Association for Advancement of Behavior Therapy. He continues to be active in contributing to the professional literature and publishing professional journal articles and book chapters.

Arthur Freeman, EdD, is professor and chair of the Department of Psychology and director of the doctoral program in clinical psychology at the Philadelphia College of Osteopathic Medicine. He is also professor in the core doctoral faculty and director of the cognitive therapy program at the Adler School of Professional Psychology in Chicago. In addition to many book chapters, reviews, and journal articles, Dr. Freeman has published 16 professional books, including *Cognitive Therapy of Personality Disorders* (with Aaron T. Beck), *Clinical Applications of Cognitive Therapy*, and *Comprehensive Casebook of Cognitive Therapy* (with Frank Dattilio). Dr. Freeman has also published two self-help books, *Woulda, Coulda, Shoulda: Overcoming Regrets, Mistakes and Missed Opportunities* (with Rose DeWolf) and *The Ten Dumbest Mistakes Smart People Make and How to Avoid Them: Simple & Sure Techniques for Gaining Greater Control of Your Life* (with Rose DeWolf). His published works have been translated into Chinese, Dutch, German, Italian, Japanese, Portuguese, Spanish, and Swedish. Dr. Freeman serves on the editorial boards of several U.S. and international journals. He continues to be one of the most in-demand lecturers and public presenters on the national and international training circuit.

He is board certified in clinical psychology and behavioral psychology by the American Board of Professional Psychology and is a fellow of the American Psychological Association (Clinical Psychology, Psychotherapy, and Family Psychology), the American Psychological Society, the Academy of Clinical Psychology, and the Pennsylvania Psychological Association. Dr. Freeman is a past president of the Association for Advancement of Behavior Therapy. He holds the distinction of having been a visiting professor of psychiatry and psychology at the Universities of Umeå and Gothenburg (Sweden), the University of Catania (Italy), and the Shanghai Second Medical University (China).

Acknowledgments

When Aaron T. Beck first began to develop his work on depression in the early 1960s, he also began a revolution in understanding and treating this common human condition. Over the past decades, his work in cognitive therapy has evolved in clinical sophistication, empirical support, and popularity. The International Association for Cognitive Psychotherapy and several professional journals are now dedicated to the advancement and dissemination of the cognitive-behavioral model. Both authors have had the good fortune of being trained at the Center for Cognitive Therapy at the University of Pennsylvania under his wise guidance. We are grateful for what he has offered to us and, by extension, to the clinical community.

The authors are also grateful to The Psychological Corporation for giving us the opportunity to craft the materials contained in this workbook. As project directors, Sandra Prince-Embury, PhD, and Tom Cayton, PhD, have overseen its growth. We thank Dr. Prince-Embury for revising and restructuring the workbook to enhance its clinical applications and for overseeing the completion of the project. Stephanie Tong, Research Assistant, has also worked diligently on this client workbook, offering many valuable suggestions. The editorial staff has contributed to making the materials easy to read without sacrificing our unique "voice" and clinical ideas.

A special note of appreciation goes to another person who has delivered messages of hope in times of hardship, Pete Seeger, who has sung songs such as *We Shall Overcome* and *Turn, Turn, Turn.* Pete also offered suggestions for this book. His messages (and his life) of perseverance during times of unfairness and struggle have helped many. Simple ideas and sincerity of purpose can move mountains, and Pete has taught many people to hold on in the midst of unhappiness and suffering. We also wish to thank Sing Out! Publications for letting us include an excerpt from the Sing Out! Publications book *Where Have All the Flowers Gone* by Pete Seeger. We also extend much thanks to our illustrator, Joseph Duffy, who provided the fanciful illustrations of the Depression Beast.

We would also like to use this opportunity to acknowledge the personal and professional support of M. Jane Yates, PhD, and Sharon E. Freeman, who have nurtured and encouraged our creative endeavor each step of the way. Dr. Yates also reviewed the workbook extensively and offered much expertise. In addition, we wish to thank our students, without whose incisive questions many of our ideas and much of our technical work would not have developed as they have. Finally, Mark Gilson would like to dedicate this book to his parents, Rhea and Nathan. We are pleased to be able to offer this workbook to you, the reader.

Beginning Questions and Answers

The goals of this chapter are to understand

- the general outline of the program
- the symptoms of depression
- the types of depression
- how the primacy and recency effects influence your experiences
- the BEAST metaphor for depression

A General Overview of Depression

Depression is a familiar emotion to most people. You may be familiar with depression because a loved one has suffered from it. You may know about depression because of what you have read in newspapers and magazines. You may see programs and information about it on TV. You may have called it "the blues," "feeling down," being "out of sorts," or just feeling "negative," but depression is no stranger to most of us. The effects of depression may include emotional symptoms such as sadness and physical symptoms such as loss of appetite; people who are depressed may simply want to be left alone, or they may hide from the world. For some people, depression brings feelings of hopelessness and a sense that things will never get better. In severe situations, some individuals plan or even attempt suicide.

Depression is a broad term used to describe a variety of experiences, symptoms, and emotions. Associated with depression are behaviors such as avoidance of pleasurable activities and lack of motivation. Sometimes even everyday things are difficult, such as going to work, paying bills, caring for personal hygiene, getting out of bed, or leaving the house. Sleep patterns may be disrupted. For instance, a depressed person may wake up too early, have difficulty falling asleep, or wake up in the middle of the night. Sex may become uninteresting and may be avoided. Appetite may decrease, leading to unwanted weight loss, or appetite may increase, leading to unwanted weight gain.

Depression appears without invitation. Sometimes depression is a reaction to some life experience, such as the death of a loved one. This kind of reactive depression is to be expected and is usually short-lived. Other times, depression may come for no clear reason and stay far longer than anticipated. Some people believe they are depressed all the time. For these people, feelings of happiness are an illusion, and reality is seen through a dark filter of depressive misery.

Perhaps you are reading this client workbook because you or someone you know may be experiencing depression. If this is the case, these descriptions are probably all too familiar. You may have dealt with depression in the past. The good news is that working with your therapist and using this workbook as part of therapy will put you on the road to recovering from depression. You will begin taking charge of your life by learning specific techniques for coping with depression if it returns. Depression can be limited in its effects, shortened in its duration, and defeated.

What Makes This Program Different?

What makes this program for treating depression different from other programs or previous therapy? You may be saying to yourself, "I've tried to deal with depression before, and it didn't work" or "I've been in therapy, so why will this be different?" This program is based on a psychotherapy called cognitive therapy (CT). We will explain exactly what that means as we go through the program. An important fact that you should know about cognitive therapy is that it is one of the most effective therapies available for the treatment of depression (Dobson, 1989). In fact, this therapy can be at least as effective as antidepressant medication in treating depression. If medication is prescribed, cognitive therapy is a useful supplement to the medicine to decrease the likelihood that depression will recur.

How Does the Program Work?

This program is based on the idea that when you are depressed, your own internal processes are at work. The good part of this is that you can also use those internal processes to feel better.

Our first goal is to help you develop skills to identify the specific pieces that go into depression. Very often, this involves understanding the thinking patterns associated with depressed mood. Understanding the connection between your negative thinking, low moods, and withdrawn behavior is essential. Next, we will begin to work on making *changes in your life*. This problem-focused approach asks you to track how you think and what you do between sessions and then work on strategies for change. The pace is set using the teamwork relationship between *you* and your *therapist*.

Everyone is different, and we recommend that you work with your therapist or counselor to tailor different techniques to your own particular needs. Later on, going back to some of the sections in which you may have experienced some difficulty may be useful. At the end of each chapter is a review section designed to help you gauge your understanding of the ideas presented and monitor your progress. If you find that the questions are difficult, go back to the relevant sections in the chapter and reread them until you can answer the questions at the end. Do not hesitate to talk with your therapist about the review questions and about sections of the chapter that are unclear.

Throughout this workbook, we will be asking you to think about things differently than you may be used to. We will ask you to write thoughts down, try new activities, and talk about things. Through this process, you will begin to take control of your life by taking small, easily managed steps. *You don't have to worry about doing everything at once.*

Individuals who have depression frequently report, "My family thinks that I'm not really depressed enough for therapy. They think that I just need to perk up (get a job, get a hobby, get out more, get a pet). What do I do?" For now, remember that *you* are the one who is experiencing a depressive change in mood. Only you can really know the severity of your depression and whether you want to change this situation for yourself. This program will help you identify your depression and assess your motivation to change it.

What Is Depression?

Depression is sometimes called the common cold of emotional problems because most people have experienced it at some time in their lives. You are not alone in your depression. It is estimated that 17.6 million Americans suffer from depression each year (National Institutes of Health, 1997). Depression can be far more disabling than medical illnesses such as chronic lung disease, arthritis, and diabetes. Although these facts and statistics are startling, the subjective experience of depression can be overwhelming. The important fact for you now is that the problem of depression has been identified, and there is something you can do about it.

Like the common cold, in the past few years newer and more effective treatments to relieve depression have been developed. These treatments can teach you to improve your thinking so that you may live a more fulfilling life. This program was developed to help you cope more effectively with the problem of depression and other mood disorders. This client workbook was designed to enhance your efforts to improve your life by first gaining control over your mood.

As we mentioned before, the term *depression* describes a number of problems. We are going to work on your specific problems by starting with general complaints. Recognizing general complaints will help you and your therapist identify specific areas in which your thoughts have become depressive. We are going to locate reasons for your depression.

You may wonder if there is a difference between being in a bad mood and being depressed. Everyone gets in a bad mood now and then. Many times, it is nothing to worry about. However, if your bad mood persists for days or weeks, you become depressed frequently, or your low points of depression are extreme, you may need to see a professional therapist to get a more thorough evaluation. Following are examples of individuals who found themselves struggling with depression. Do any of these descriptions sound familiar?

Case Examples

James

James, a supervisor at a car assembly plant, came to therapy after his employer downsized and he was laid off. He found himself having trouble reading, talking to his wife, and just getting up in the morning. He no longer enjoyed activities that he used to look forward to, like playing cards, watching TV, and bowling. He began to avoid contact with friends and ignore his family. When he and his therapist took notice of his thinking (or *cognitions*), they discovered that when he felt bad he would first think about how terrible it was to be out of work. The negative thinking then generalized to thoughts such as "I never really was competent to work in a responsible job" and "I am a failure at everything I have ever tried."

Sadness turned into grief, and grief turned into depression. James and his therapist began to work on identifying and disputing the negative thinking he had about himself and his life. While he was in his worst mood, James ignored the advantages of his layoff. He had left his job with severance pay of 1 year's full salary and benefits while he looked for another job. Some may say he had no reason to feel bad. However, James had a strong belief that it was shameful to be asked to leave a position that he had held for 15 years. Challenging such a belief and the thoughts associated with it was the starting point that led James to recover from depression. He rediscovered the people he loved and began to pursue a change in career.

Betty

Betty was 32 years old and recently divorced. She had a 4-year-old child and had to balance work and day care. She started to feel that nothing was going to go right for her *ever again.* She found herself going through the same daily routine. By the time weekends came, she was too tired and unmotivated to maintain her household. Watching television had been her favorite way to relax, and she found that she no longer derived enjoyment from that. She withdrew from friends and sensed that there was no pleasure for her in anything. The less she did, the worse she felt. She had trouble getting to sleep and frequently woke up hours before her alarm clock was set to go off. Her eating patterns became irregular, and her diet consisted mostly of junk food, which led to a weight gain. Her mood was affecting her child. She started to wish she was dead and finally sought treatment at her parents' urging.

Ellen

For Ellen, the situation was completely different. She had no divorce, no job loss, and no hard times. She was married to a warm, supportive husband. Her children were both in college and doing well. Her parents were retired and healthy. She enjoyed good relationships with her brother and two sisters. She worked at a part-time job she liked with people she liked. She lived in a nice house in a nice neighborhood and had a very comfortable life. You might ask, "What does she have to be depressed about?" The answer is apparently nothing. But depression does not limit itself to people with obvious problems. Ellen began having trouble getting up in the morning; she lost interest in spending time with her husband and spoke to her children only briefly by phone. The job she used to enjoy she no longer wanted. Ellen was depressed. She somehow attributed her depression to being a bad person. The reasonable punishment for her imagined badness was the depression.

If these examples sound familiar to you, you may be struggling with depression. Read on for more information.

Identifying Symptoms

Following is a chart listing the symptoms of depression. Go through the chart three times. The first time, just check the ones that apply to you. The second time, rate how severe each problem has been in your most recent depression on a scale from 1 to 10. Finally, go through the list a third time and evaluate how frequently the symptom occurs over a period of time (e.g., 1 week).

Depression Symptom Checklist

Symptom	Does Symptom Currently Apply To You? "✓" if "Yes"	Severity (1–10)*	How Often Does This Symptom Occur?
1. Low mood almost every day or part of every day for at least 2 weeks			
2. Lack of interest in activities that were once pleasurable			
3. Weight loss or gain (not from dieting) of 5% of body weight			
4. Difficulty falling or staying asleep or early awakening nearly every night			
5. Sluggishness or physical tension almost every day			
6. Fatigue or low energy almost every day			
7. Low self-esteem and a sense of worthlessness or guilt			
8. Chronic difficulty making decisions, thinking clearly, and/or keeping focused			
9. Repetitive thoughts of death and suicide and/or plans to commit suicide			
10. Symptoms seem worse in the morning, including often waking up too early			

*1 = almost nonexistent in my life
5 = applies to me about half of the time
10 = very relevant to my condition

Naming the Problem

There are many types of depression. Each is different from the others in subtle ways. The different names that are used often reflect how severe or long-standing the problem is. Some of the familiar "flavors" of depression follow.

Major Depressive Disorder

Major depressive disorder is the most common of the mood disorders. It is a serious condition that interferes with functioning and requires treatment. This depression may be experienced as a single episode or as a series of episodes. For a diagnosis of major depressive disorder, five or more of the following symptoms must be present during the same 2-week period: depressed mood *or* loss of interest *and* significant weight loss or gain or change in appetite, insomnia or hypersomnia, motor agitation or slowness, fatigue or loss of energy, feelings of worthlessness or guilt, decreased ability to concentrate or make decisions, recurrent thoughts of death or suicide.

Dysthymic Disorder

Dysthymic disorder is sometimes called "watered-down depression." A person who has dysthymic disorder experiences depressed mood for most of the day, for more days than not, for a period of at least 2 years. In addition, two or more of the following symptoms are also present: poor appetite or overeating, insomnia or hypersomnia, low energy or fatigue, low self-esteem, poor concentration or indecisiveness, feelings of hopelessness.

Adjustment Disorder with Depressed Mood

The depression that occurs with adjustment disorder is usually directly related to a particular life problem and a person's difficulty in adjusting to it. The depressed mood usually occurs within 3 months of the onset of the stressor. The symptoms cause either marked distress or significant impairment.

Mood Disorder Due to a General Medical Condition, with Depressive Features

As the name implies, this type of depression is due to a physical illness. The possibility of such a cause emphasizes the need for a medical evaluation to eliminate (or treat) the medical condition as a factor in the depression.

Substance-Induced Mood Disorder, with Depressive Features

Use of alcohol or other drugs (especially "downers") can cause depressive–like symptoms. Withdrawal from cocaine, amphetamines, alcohol, or barbiturates can also contribute to depression.

Bipolar Disorder

One of the more serious mood disorders involving depression is bipolar disorder, which is often better known by its former name, manic depression. Bipolar disorder includes mood changes that occur in cycles with "highs" or manic periods that give way to periods of intense depression. It usually includes some period when mood becomes balanced between the periods of depression and mania. In a manic phase, people feel exhilarated to the degree that they may become grandiose and have unrealistic beliefs about their abilities. If you are feeling depressed right now, you might say to yourself that it would be wonderful to feel so great. Actually, with this "too good" feeling, agitation and irritability are very common. These symptoms often lead to high-risk behaviors such as going over budget with credit cards, making dangerous and speculative investments, engaging in sexual indiscretions, and other activities that could lead to painful consequences. For some individuals, these "high" symptoms may become so severe that hospitalization is necessary because of their lack of sleep or inability to care responsibly for themselves and their families.

Other Mood Problems

One form of low mood is referred to as realistic depression, grief, or bereavement. If you have suffered serious losses or dramatic changes in your life recently and are feeling down as a result, you may be experiencing a natural reaction that many people go through. As natural aspects of human experience, such periods of sadness are not viewed as a form of depression unless they are unusually severe, are present for an extended period, or cause significant distress and impairment.

Regardless of the exact title of your depression, the essential similarity of the different types of depression allows us to deal with them all in a similar fashion. Any form of depression may have an impact on work and relationships, some more severely than others and some for briefer times than others. All depression involves a negative view of the world (the belief that the world is a horrible place), a negative view of self (low self-esteem), and a negative view of the future (the belief that things will never improve). We will talk about this in greater detail in the next chapter.

Telling Thoughts of Self-Harm

At some point, all of us think about getting away from it all. For some, that means getting into bed and pulling the covers up. For others, it may take the form of a vacation to a favorite place. For others, it might mean a visit to a church, synagogue, or other place of refuge. For some, however, getting away from it all means the ultimate escape through death. If at any time you have thoughts of harming yourself or someone else, you must immediately contact your physician, therapist, or local crisis center. Suicidal wishes are a common and potentially lethal problem for many people who are depressed and for their families.

This program is designed to help you find appropriate and helpful alternatives to such drastic action. Some people feel that talking about suicidal thoughts may make the idea seem more acceptable. Because they feel embarrassed about having them, others keep them a secret. Our experience is that talking openly about such thoughts can help you view them more objectively and may provide you with some immediate relief. Remember that your relationship with your therapist is based on trust. That trust and the investment of your time and effort are what will help you feel better. Talk with your therapist about any thoughts or impulses you may be having or may have had regarding suicide or harming yourself.

Depression When It Is Most Dangerous: Suicidal Thoughts

Depression is a dangerous creature when it tries to attack your sense of hope. Loss of hope develops when your reasons for being alive are threatened by negative thoughts about the future. For some individuals, loss of hope about the future is so severe that they consider killing themselves to solve or escape problems. Suicide is sometimes described as a permanent solution to temporary problems. When not confronted directly, thoughts about suicide may appear to provide a way out of emotional pain, physical pain, unrelenting pressure, or embarrassing situations. This is a false impression and a symptom of depression that must be challenged.

The following questions are designed to measure how much you suffer from loss of hope. For each question, score 1 for not at all, 2 for rarely, 3 for sometimes, 4 for often, and 5 for all the time. If you answer 2, 3, 4, or 5 to any of them, contact your therapist and discuss the feelings and thoughts you are having. Sometimes you may need another person to help you challenge loss of hope when you have lost the strength to do so yourself.

1. I have thoughts of killing myself. _________
2. I have plans to kill myself. _________
3. I feel hopeless about the future. _________
4. I think no one would miss me if I died. _________
5. I think that if I kill myself, others will see how much I hurt. _________
6. I think there is no reason for me to live. _________
7. I am a burden to others. _________
8. It seems that things will never get any better. _________
9. It seems that any hope that I once had is now gone. _________
10. Nothing matters anymore. _________

Add up your total score. If your score is 20 or higher or if you responded 3 or more to question 2, talk to a mental health professional right away.

Stories of Hope

The actor Christopher Reeve played the role of Superman in the movies. He had (and has) every feature of a courageous hero. In the movies, the man of steel was practically invulnerable to the forces that could injure or defeat mere mortals. Only the rare substance kryptonite could weaken him. In real life, Reeve fell from a horse and was paralyzed as a result of the accident that broke his neck. He has no movement below his neck and is not able to breathe without mechanical help. He is no longer able to get around or take care of himself without assistance. However, a year after his accident, he was interviewed about his recovery. Many people who know about Reeve's plight questioned themselves about whether they would have wanted to live after such tragic loss of physical functions. How could he go on?

Reeve's statements in that interview indicated that he had once had the kind of hopeless thinking you may be experiencing. However, he began making decisions that led him to choose life over death. His reasons for choosing life were based on his situation and values, but more important is the fact that he confronted this decision in the face of circumstances that would have caused many people to lose hope.

Pete Seeger, the folk singer who writes about struggle, change, and hope, including songs such as "We Shall Overcome" and "Turn, Turn, Turn," often tells the following story at his concerts (Seeger & Blood, 1997). A man is walking in the forest when a tiger jumps out from behind the bushes and begins to chase him. The man runs as fast as he can, but the hungry tiger is gaining ground. If he is caught, the beast will certainly kill and eat him. Ahead of him is a cliff. If he stops running, he will die. If he jumps, who knows? He decides to jump. When he does, he catches a branch on the way down. The branch starts to crack. On the side of the cliff, he sees a ripe strawberry and takes a bite. The man thinks to himself, "This is the sweetest thing I have ever had in my life." The essential aspect about adversity is that you do not know what will come next. Hope is possible, even in the most serious of circumstances.

Finding reasons to stay alive is a challenge that anyone who deals with depression may face. The effort to find reasons to live represents the direction of this workbook and your therapy. You can find satisfying ways to convert the strongest feelings of outrage and hurt into meaningful, life-enhancing activities and interactions. Reeve provides a dramatic example. By actively confronting loss of hope and enhancing the skills you will develop through therapy, it is possible to overcome many adversities, even in severe circumstances.

What Influences Your Experiences: The Primacy and Recency Effects

If you are asked how you feel, chances are you would answer according to how you are feeling right now (the *recency* effect). When you are feeling down or depressed, you may feel that you have always felt this way and have trouble remembering better times. Many times depression seems to dictate that any "better" moods are illusions and that the real world is limited to the darkness of depression. Depression also often goes along with feeling overwhelmed. Research on mood problems indicates that global self-assessment is usually influenced by two types of effects on experience: primacy and recency.

Primacy effect refers to the observation that events from early in your memory influence how you experience the present. For example, if a schoolteacher mistreated you early in your education, you are likely to feel uncomfortable around other teachers, even in situations in which you have not been mistreated. This expectation may lead to avoidance of teachers or avoidance of school altogether. This avoidance can be self-defeating by sustaining the expectation that you will be mistreated.

Recency effect refers to the observation that the most recent events in your life have a particularly strong effect on your general attitude toward yourself, your situation, and the future. The following example illustrates the recency effect. You are driving to meet someone, and on the way another driver changes lanes and crashes into your front fender. After you finish the accident report with the police, you go on to meet your friend. Do you think the recency of your traffic accident would affect how you feel when you finally get to see your friend? Most people are apt to be in a less than pleasant mood or at least distracted. The emotions that you experience in reaction to your most recent experiences may produce similar emotions when you react to events that closely follow.

How Can I Fight What I Can't See? The BEAST Metaphor

Your therapy will treat your depression more effectively if you know and understand the enemy. We use a metaphor to describe depression as the BEAST. The BEAST is a metaphor in that it suggests a similarity between depression and a beast. Using the BEAST metaphor, you can think of depression as the process that results in sapped energy, diminished pleasure, and reduced motivation. The BEAST metaphor may help you see problems of depression as separate from who you are as a person. You can then use this metaphor to see yourself as the person who can tame the BEAST of depression.

Understanding the BEAST of Depression

Depression is not one single problem. Rather, it is a combination of many different aspects and issues. In addition to using BEAST as a metaphor, you can also use the word as an acronym to remember the various aspects of depression. An acronym is

a word made up of the first letter of each word in a phrase or list. The BEAST represents the following components of depression:

- Body (biology and biochemistry)
- Emotion (how you feel)
- Action (what you do)
- Situation (your immediate life experiences)
- Thoughts (how and what you think)

Each of these components is important in understanding depression and how it is maintained. By looking at each of these parts, you can start to shrink the bigger-than-life-size BEAST of depression down to a size you can manage. There is much more to say about the BEAST, so read on.

Now that you understand how the BEAST represents the different aspects of depression, let's start working on overcoming it. Recognize that there is more to recovering from depression than simply deciding to do it. There are forces pulling in many directions. One force says, "Get going"; another says, "Sit and wait. It will go away." Yet another force says, "Nothing that you do will change anything."

Self-Enhancement Assignments

To help you combat forces that may conflict with your goals for therapy, we have included self-enhancement assignments (assignments that you do on your own) in each section. They are designed to enhance what you learn in therapy and to contribute to your improvement. The new skills that you learn through this program and with your therapist are like any other skills: Your performance improves with practice. The self-enhancement assignments provide that practice.

What If I'm Too Depressed to Do This?

One of the thinking errors people with depression make is relying on their mistaken belief that nothing will work out for them. Then, on the basis of this idea, they give up before they make an effort. If you are like this, you are probably experiencing a symptom of depression. To challenge the symptom, consider the scientific concept that theories are not valid until they are tested. When you do not work on self-enhancement assignments, you are relying on an untested theory. Try the exercises before you assume that they will not work for you.

Will Medication Help Me?

For many people, medication is an important part of the overall psychotherapy plan. If you are severely depressed, medication may be an essential part of helping you reach a level where you can use other forms of therapy. For some individuals, such as those with bipolar disorder, medication is essential. However, in the treatment of more typical unipolar depression, medication may or may not be indicated. Whether to begin or continue to take medication for your mood is ultimately your decision. Consultation, agreement, and communication with your psychiatrist or family physician are essential for your continued health. Do not begin, alter, or stop medication without first consulting your physician.

Keeping Track: How Can I Tell If I Am Improving?

To ensure that you know when change has taken place, you must first know how you are doing *before* you begin the program. You will be learning throughout the program how to step back and reflect on how you are doing. This part of the evaluation process lets you know where you were when you started and how far you have come. An important part of the program addresses how you can keep track of your daily life (Chapter 5) so that you have a better idea of just what you are (or are not) doing with your day. In another section of the program (Chapter 6), you will learn to record situations in which you experience a particularly low mood.

All of these parts of the program are intended to help you learn when, how, and sometimes why you get depressed. They will also help you understand how you react to these situations and circumstances. Once you have a clear picture of these factors, you will begin to see how this program and your own effort can change your mood. Learning how to keep track of these different aspects of your life can help to improve your mood, especially when you look back and see the progress you have made.

Do you know why you are depressed? Many people who have mood disorders seem to look for a single explanation to get at the root of their problem. Mood disorders can cause much distress, so it is not surprising that you would want to find a quick cure. But where do you look? Some say that the only way to understand and deal with depression is first to look back on the past. By going through this search, you may come up with some insight that may lift your depression. This program does not take this approach. Instead, you will learn how to change your negative thinking now to relieve your current depression and prevent future depression.

As mentioned before, a basic principle of this program is that you are going to be focusing more on looking ahead to where you are going, rather than back at where you have been. The second principle is that there are specific reasons for your low mood that you can identify and change. It is important to understand, however, that your problems probably will not be solved by a sudden burst of insight that will immediately change your mood. Identifying specific problems is a gradual process of small insights that contribute to understanding your depression.

How Long Will This Program Take?

Given how bad you may feel, it is understandable that you may want to be over your depression as quickly as possible. In many ways, our culture focuses on quick fixes. If life was like a TV show, a life-threatening problem or breakdown would be fixed in one episode. The crew of a ship (starship, airship, ocean-going ship) is in danger, and in 60 minutes they are saved (along with the world or universe as well, sometimes). In reality, these situations and the related thinking are unrealistic and can set you up for disappointment.

There are ways to repair some aspects of your life rather quickly. More realistically, weeks or months are needed to manage the BEAST of depression and start to take control. Keep in mind that this period is usually less time than it takes for depression to develop.

An important question that you must think about is this: Are you ready to take charge of and deal with your depression? It takes energy to stay depressed, and it takes effort to divert the energy that keeps you from changing. Each time you decide to try the assignments in this book, you make a courageous decision to move away from depression toward more effective ways of thinking, feeling, and acting. It also takes effort to avoid doing the things that may get you into a dark emotional hole. The choices are yours to make, with the help of your therapist and this program. It is your courage to change at a pace that fits you that will make a difference. Like many things in life, you won't get the benefit unless you get involved, and we cannot overemphasize the importance of doing the self-enhancement assignments.

The speed with which you and your therapist work through this workbook and your treatment is based on many factors, including the severity of your depression, your motivation to change, the time you can put into changing, the distractions and interferences you experience, and, most important, how willing you are to stick to the program. Although some people may benefit from daily or weekly work, others may benefit more by a slower pace. You will decide how quickly to move along. You can discuss this with your therapist and gauge yourself by a standard that fits you. This program and the information you acquire are for lifelong improvement. It is designed to give you a chance to understand your thinking and challenge the old beliefs that have kept you down in the past. Take as much time as you need.

Some of you may be excited by the prospect of taking control and beating the BEAST of your depression at its own game. Others of you may be discouraged and saying, "I've been here before. I've tried other programs. I've tried therapy. I have a dozen books on my shelf at home that have made the same promises." Do not let a negative view prevent your recovery from depression. Take charge!

How Do I Get Started?

To begin our work, we will return to the BEAST metaphor.

- B = Body
- E = Emotion
- A = Action
- S = Situation
- T = Thoughts

The first steps involve tracking or identifying the BEAST. What is the BEAST? What are the effects of Body, Emotion, Action, Situation, and Thoughts when you are feeling low? Each of these elements contributes to the overall picture of depression. Instead of asking these questions in the dark, the workbook gives you a means to hunt these interrelated problems with minimum effort and maximum results as you start the program. As you identify and control each part, the BEAST becomes more controllable and has less effect on your life. For each of the following statements, identify which particular problems you experience. Each statement begins with the letter that links it to the BEAST acronym. After you have completed this exercise, look at which aspects of depression are the most problematic for you.

	Yes	No
B1. I feel physically ill, but my doctor has trouble identifying medical problems.	_______	_______
B2. I am generally fatigued.	_______	_______
B3. I experience muscle aches and pains.	_______	_______
B4. I tend to get headaches.	_______	_______
B5. I have digestive problems.	_______	_______
E6. I am sad most of the time.	_______	_______
E7. I cry a lot.	_______	_______
E8. There are very few times when I feel happy.	_______	_______
E9. Depression is just my way of life.	_______	_______
E10. I will be sad forever.	_______	_______
A11. I am too tired to do anything.	_______	_______
A12. I cannot get started.	_______	_______
A13. There is nothing I can do to change my depression.	_______	_______
A14. I have no motivation.	_______	_______
A15. I am not interested in contact with other people.	_______	_______

		Yes	No
S16.	My situation cannot be changed.	_______	_______
S17.	My relationships cause me great pain.	_______	_______
S18.	My relationships are falling apart.	_______	_______
S19.	My life's work is a waste of time.	_______	_______
S20.	I am controlled by situations.	_______	_______
T21.	I am a loser.	_______	_______
T22.	I fail more than most people do.	_______	_______
T23.	This will not work.	_______	_______
T24.	Nothing will change me.	_______	_______
T25.	I will never be able to take control of my life.	_______	_______

Motivation for Change

A good way to begin this program is to assess your level of motivation. To do this, answer the following questions about your motivation for change.

Reasons to Change

	True	False
I want to enjoy life more.	○	○
My sleep patterns are not right.	○	○
I think about killing myself, but I do not really want to.	○	○
I would like to have good relationships.	○	○

	True	False
I want to concentrate better.	○	○
I want to be less irritable.	○	○
I want more energy.	○	○
I would like to control my weight.	○	○
I want to like myself.	○	○
I would like to enjoy sex again.	○	○

If you answered true to at least seven of these questions, you have the motivation necessary to change. If you answered true to fewer than seven of these questions, you might want to discuss your motivation for change with your therapist. In beginning this program, it is important that you are motivated to change. Remember, you are the only one who can choose to take control and overcome your depression.

The following chapters are designed to help you recognize the BEAST, take action to tame the BEAST, and build on your progress toward change. It is important to work with your therapist to tailor different methods to meet your needs. You will be able to review and master areas where you may have experienced some difficulty.

Chapter 1 Review

Try answering the following questions.

1. Name three typical symptoms of depression.

2. What are the parts of the BEAST?

   B =

   E =

   A =

   S =

   T =

3. How long will the program take to complete?

4. How are sadness and depression different?

5. How common is depression?

6. The powerful force that influences our perception in which something that just happened is most easily remembered is called the _________ effect.

7. The powerful force that influences our perception in which something that happened very early in the process is most easily remembered is called the _________ effect.

The Theory and Practice of Cognitive Therapy

The goals of this chapter are to understand

- the theory of cognitive therapy (CT)
- the elements of depression from the CT perspective
- the cognitive triad
- the elements of cognitive distortions
- the role of schema in depression

The Theory of Cognitive Therapy

This program is based on cognitive therapy (CT), a model of psychotherapy developed by Aaron T. Beck. It is one of several cognitive-behavioral models of therapy (Beck, 1983; Beck & Freeman, 1990; Beck, Rush, Shaw, & Emery, 1979) that include the pioneering works of Albert Ellis (Ellis, 1973; Ellis & Harper, 1975), Arnold Lazarus (1976), and Donald Meichenbaum (Meichenbaum & Turk, 1987). The major focus of CT is to help you examine how you understand the world (your cognitions) and to help you experiment with new ways of responding (your behaviors). Understanding the unique way you perceive yourself, your life experiences, and your prospects for the future can help you alter depression and behave more adaptively.

The cognitive model of depression in this program is based on the tendency of people who are depressed to perceive themselves, their situation, and their future in a negative way. If you are like most individuals who are depressed, you tend to view yourself as inadequate, incapable, and unlovable.

You might also believe that others reject you and criticize you. You may view your future as bleak and hopeless. Given this belief system, your apathy and lowered

energy levels are not surprising. If you believe your efforts will be fruitless, it would make sense to conserve your energy and to spare work that will result in failure. This pattern of thinking has been observed among adults, adolescents, and children who are experiencing depression.

In a research study that demonstrated how mood can affect how we see things, people were shown two pictures at once, one in either eye (Gilson, 1984). The pictures shown to one eye had negative themes and the picture flashed to the other eye had neutral or positive themes. Since the images were flashed simultaneously at a very fast speed, people usually were only able to report some of the information with which they were presented. Depressed people tended to report the most negative information and people who were not depressed tended to describe a balance of negative, neutral, and positive aspects of what they saw. It appeared that people who were depressed were accurate, but selectively negative in how they processed the information they were given. In a similar study, participants were presented with negative and neutral words. People who were depressed tended to recognize a higher proportion of negative words than those who were not depressed (Powell & Hemsley, 1984). You have only so much energy to use to focus on a world full of positive, negative, and neutral options. Emotional bias suggests that your priorities for the options you decide to select or reject might be based on how you feel (Clark, Fairburn, & Gelder, 1997). These results are important for understanding what may help people who are depressed.

Elements of Depression

Cognitive therapy helps to identify emotions and behavior patterns, as well as the thoughts and beliefs that maintain them. Once these thoughts and patterns are identified, it is possible to actively change your behavior, adapt more functionally to your world, and feel better. Within the cognitive model, affect, behavior, physiological processes, environmental events, and thoughts are seen as interacting components that influence one another.

There are five basic principles of the cognitive therapy model.

1. The way you interpret experiences, events, and situations directly influences how you subsequently feel and behave and vice versa. Cognitions (thoughts) are related to emotions and behavior.
2. This interpretation process is ongoing. It permits you to understand life events. It is goal directed and should help you function more effectively.
3. Belief systems guide behavior and influence perceptions. You may become sensitive to specific external and internal events that you experience as stressful. You may also selectively pay attention to and recall information that is consistent with your belief system. Likewise, you may selectively "overlook" information that is inconsistent with your beliefs.
4. This process of selection may impair cognitive processing. The impairment represents an attempted coping response that does not work. A system is established in which these less effective coping behaviors actually maintain negative events. In fact, this process may strengthen the maladaptive belief system.
5. The good news is that you actively organize your experiences, and you can therefore learn to use these skills to more adaptive coping. Cognitive therapy and this program give you the tools to use your experience more adaptively. You are always the important active agent.

According to cognitive theories, three major factors are involved in developing and maintaining depression: (1) the cognitive triad, (2) cognitive distortions, and (3) schemas and assumptions.

The Cognitive Triad

As discussed previously, individuals who are depressed tend to view themselves, their current experiences, and their future in an unrealistically negative manner, described by cognitive theorist Aaron Beck (1976) as the cognitive triad.

The first component of the triad is a negative view of the self. Individuals who are depressed tend to view themselves as inferior. Their thoughts are distortions by which they attribute their shortcomings to enduring, irreparable defects in personal capacities. As such, they perceive themselves as lacking the abilities necessary for gaining a sense of satisfaction. A negative self-view with accompanying self-accusations and reproaches was initially described by Sigmund Freud as an important characteristic of what we now know as depression (1917/1991).

Second, individuals who are depressed typically adopt a negative view of the world and their relationships with others. They view life as an unending struggle against recurring obstacles and see other people as critical, unsupportive, or rejecting. Because they perceive themselves as inept and their difficulties as insurmountable, they feel unworthy of others' support and anticipate rejection. Theirs is a bleak world with few rewards. These beliefs, however, are not entirely unfounded. The behavior of individuals who are depressed eventually leads to rejection and loss of others' support.

The final component of the cognitive triad centers on a pessimistic outlook for the future. Individuals who are depressed anticipate continued hardships and see little chance of success. Although there is some controversy about the presence of this component among children who are depressed, it has been observed among adolescents and adults who are depressed. Within this perspective, suicidal ideas often reflect a desire to escape what the individual perceives as an unbearable situation.

The relationship between depressive thoughts and the severity of depressive symptoms is typically strong. A research study of 81 clients in psychotherapy showed that those who were depressed had distorted thinking and misinterpreted events in terms of personal failure or rejection. Clients who were depressed also exaggerated the significance of events that seemed to reflect badly on them and maintained negative predictions that were not supported by facts. Studies documenting negative beliefs about self, world, and future among individuals who are depressed have generally supported the cognitive model (Beck, 1976).

Cognitive Distortions

An individual's thoughts can be distorted in a variety of ways. These distortions can be positive or negative. People who distort in a positive direction see the world in an unrealistically positive way—through rose-colored glasses. They lack critical judgment and may take chances that most people would wisely avoid (e.g., skydiving, investing large sums of money in a particular stock). If successful, the positive distorter is vindicated. If unsuccessful, the positive distorter may see failure as a consequence of taking a low-yield chance. Sometimes, the positive distorter takes chances that lead to situations of great danger. The positive distorter who experiences massive chest pains and does not consult a physician might reason, "I'm too young and healthy for a heart attack."

A huge amount of information surrounds you, and you must selectively attend to the information that is most valuable to your successful coping. Your capacity for selective attention, perception, and memory can serve a highly adaptive function. Cognitive theory tells us that because these cognitive processes are selective, there is a potential for distorting reality. As previously described, an individual who is depressed distorts reality in some highly dysfunctional ways. In cognitive therapy, individuals who are depressed learn to monitor these cognitive distortions and decide how to modify them.

Although the distortions related to depression are negative and can lead to dysfunctional behavior, some distortions can, under some circumstances, serve adaptive functions as well. For example, individuals who are not depressed tend to systematically overestimate their abilities and their capacity to influence outcomes (Seligman, 1991). Cognitive distortions may protect a person from the effects of uncontrollable situations. For the most part, people tend to be optimistic about their future and their ability to meet the challenges of life. Although their expectations may not always be accurate, this sense of invulnerability may serve an adaptive function. It does not hurt to be hopeful. The absence of hope leads to depression.

Although not always harmful, when unchecked, cognitive distortions can have a hazardous, negative effect, as in the most severe cases of suicidal individuals. Because cognitive distortions can contribute to significant emotional difficulties and can be identified readily, they are a legitimate focus of psychotherapy. Cognitive distortions typically do not appear in isolation but occur in combination with other thoughts. Some types of distortions overlap. This overlap reflects systematic tendencies to misinterpret events. These related cognitive distortions are so automatic that they are difficult to identify without therapy.

One common theme of misinterpretation involves self-evaluation. Depression may be related to an individual's tendency to adopt goals or standards that are unreasonably high or from an increased sensitivity to variations from one's own standards. This theme may begin early in life from parental expectations or when a traumatic event, an environmental stressor, or a loss initiates a depressive episode. Following specific events, people may experience a heightened state of self-awareness, and becoming increasingly aware of their inability to meet standards of coping, people may accept greater responsibility for negative events and outcomes. This may serve a psychological defensive function of internal control in the face of uncontrollable external events. This is consistent with Beck's (1967; 1976) emphasis on cognitive distortions such as magnification among individuals who are depressed. This serves as a powerful example of how depression is thus characterized by a tendency to overgeneralize from single, specific failures to a broader sense of personal inadequacy.

Similarly, individuals who are depressed blame themselves more than do those who are not depressed; that is, they have an increased tendency to attribute failures or negative events to character deficits (which cannot be controlled) rather than to their behavior (which can be controlled). Individuals who are depressed typically manifest high levels of pessimism and the idea that important outcomes are uncontrollable or unattainable.

Schemas

Cognitive distortions are both reflections of and are maintained by your schemas, the product of related sets of beliefs serving as a framework for your life. Although you may not be directly aware of your schemas, they underlie and maintain your belief system and thoughts that occur automatically. Schemas are arranged in a hierarchy (from less important to more important) and include a coordinated set of abstract ideas about self, world, and relationships. Your beliefs and coping mechanisms are derived from these schemas. Schemas direct your attention and influence your perception; the way you interpret information. Your cognitive schemas influence the content of your beliefs, automatic thoughts, and the process by which this information is retrieved and used. The schemas become, in effect, how you define yourself. The schemas can be active or dormant, with the more active schemas represented by those rules that govern day-to-day behavior. The dormant schemas are typically called into play to control behavior in times of stress. Schemas may be either compelling or noncompelling. The more compelling the schema, the more likely it is that you will respond to it.

Your schemas are actively developed and serve an adaptive function in that they help you efficiently evaluate your circumstances and guide coping attempts. They are the unspoken rules that you live by and typically are not open to evaluation. Schemas and assumptions are established in early childhood and are refined and consolidated by later experiences. The extent to which a schema affects your life depends on several factors: (1) how strongly held the schema is, (2) how the schema is linked with your well-being or existence, (3) the amount of questioning you engage in when a particular schema is activated, (4) your previous learning about the importance and essential nature of a particular schema, and (5) how early in your life a particular schema developed.

Although schemas are in one sense permanent, they must also be in a constant state of change to succeed in being adaptive. From a child's earliest years, there is a need to alter old schemas and develop new schemas to meet the increasingly complex demands of the world. An infant's developing concept of reality is governed by limited interaction with the world, so the infant may initially perceive the world as the crib and the mother (or others who care for the infant). As infants master the additional skills of mobility and interaction, they then perceive their world as significantly larger. This process of altering schemas to better fit new experiences is called *accommodation* (Piaget, 1966).

You use old rules as long as they work and change them only when you have to. When you encounter a new situation, you use old learning to try to cope with it. If the old learning works, you have no need to make changes, and you continue in your old pattern. If the old methods do not work, you make a slight change. If the change works, you make no further changes. If this small change does not work, you may make successively larger changes until you reach the desired effect. Schemas then become self-selective because you may ignore environmental stimuli that you are not able to integrate. Some individuals may persist in using old structures without fitting them to the new circumstances in which they are involved. Thus they may further fail to accommodate or build new cognitive structures for understanding the world.

The schemas of individuals who are depressed frequently center on specific themes of vulnerability to loss or abandonment and on personal inadequacy. Although these schemas may not be active much of the time, they can be activated by specific negative life events. These schemas of vulnerability, then, may be seen as causal factors that make people vulnerable to depression under similar circumstances.

Further evidence for the role of schemas in depressive disorders comes from the field of social psychology. Individuals who are depressed may possess an attributional style (a characteristic way of understanding cause-and-effect) that contributes to ongoing feelings of vulnerability. Schemas of hopelessness and self-reproach are frequently cardinal symptoms of depression, and are believed to be activated by someone's perception of a personally meaningful deprivation, loss, or disappointment.

For example, Debbie, a 26-year-old single woman, became highly depressed and suicidal after her boyfriend of 1 month left her for another woman. Her specific thoughts centered on themes of loss, personal inadequacy, and the necessity of romantic relationships to her sense of self-worth. These beliefs appear to have been long-standing. Debbie was the youngest of six children and had been unplanned. Her parents had vowed to have no more after five, and had told her that she was unwanted because her older brother had been so difficult. She described her father as critical and unsupportive of her mother and the female children in her family. Debbie's cognitive distortions included magnification of personal deficits such as physical attractiveness (which was highly valued because of its importance in attracting men), minimization of personal attributes, and selective inattention to positive experiences.

This example illustrates how cognitive schemas and assumptions are based on individuals' life experiences and perceptions, which are highly personal and idiosyncratic. Nonetheless, beliefs and assumptions may be shared by people with similar experiences and may be widely accepted by specific social or cultural groups.

Assumptions and schemas can, under specific circumstances, become a wellspring from which cognitive distortions and maladaptive beliefs emerge. Although they may be latent much of the time, schemas may be activated by external events that are similar to the experiences that contributed to their establishment. When activated, specific beliefs, distortions, and styles of thinking become apparent. An individual's assumptions and beliefs are of various strengths. The person's degree of belief in them and their importance to the person's sense of self determine the extent to which a schema may serve as a source of cognitive distortions.

How you respond to the activation of specific schemas can change their effect on your emotions. If you have the belief, for example, that "people should always love me," you might become dependent and helpless, always seeking support and reassurance, and continually vigilant for signs of others' lack of interest or annoyance. Alternatively, such an individual might become an outstanding college professor, actor, or politician who constantly seeks approval.

The manner in which you respond to the activation of a schema influences the feedback you will receive from others and from your environment. This feedback—and your selective attention to it—serves to consolidate your belief system. Individuals do not simply attach meaning to environmental events. Rather, they approach situations and events in a goal-directed (yet unrecognized) manner and actively develop the situation to make it consistent with the belief system. In this way, maladaptive schemas are further validated.

Schemas may be based on a range of issues. They appear to include beliefs about self, relationships with others, the world, and the future. The schemas of a person who is depressed might include beliefs such as "I am unlovable" and "Life is a continuous struggle." Clinical syndromes may be distinguished in terms of the specific content of the underlying belief system. As we have noted previously, the beliefs of individuals who are depressed typically center on themes of personal inadequacy and vulnerability to loss.

The process of clarifying and resolving maladaptive schemas is central to cognitive therapy and this program. As the faulty schemas that underlie your depressive episodes are understood and resolved, your potential for depression relapse is reduced because life is no longer filtered through networks of negative beliefs.

Chapter 2 Review

1. Identify from which area your own cognitive distortions most likely arise (i.e., yourself, your situation, the future).

2. Can cognitive distortions ever be useful or helpful? How?

3. Name the three parts of the cognitive triad and how they affect you.

4. Identify at least two basic rules of life or schemas that you have.

5. How do schemas affect your behavior?

Understanding Your Body: The B of the BEAST

The goals of this chapter are to understand

- the interaction of the body and depression
- how diet and nutrition affect depression
- how health problems can add to or cause depression
- the effects of brain chemistry on depression
- how medication can help

In the past several decades, great advances have been made in understanding brain chemistry, bodily reactions, and depression. Affect problems have a significant physical dimension, just as physical problems may have a significant affective component. Every major physical system of your body can be affected by depression and can, in turn, contribute to it. You may feel weak (muscular system), experience stomach or bowel upset (digestive system), and feel shaky, tingly, or dizzy (neurological system). You may lose your sexual urge (reproductive system), have the need to urinate frequently (urinary system), or sweat more than usual (dermal system).

The Biology of Depression

Some of the best methods for dealing with the physical aspect of the BEAST are the most direct. Rather than sitting around waiting for the depression to lift and for the physical symptoms to stop, you can go right to the heart of the problem. You must respect your body with proper diet, exercise, and sufficient sleep. Your first response may be to say, "If I could do those things, I wouldn't need this book." You are right, in a way, at this point in your life. However, you might have been able to do them at some previous point without any help. We are going to work at reestablishing the patterns that work best for you.

Mood and Diet

Sometimes you may have trouble eating because your insides feel as though they are in a knot. For many of you, loss of appetite is the first sign of depression. If the depression is mild, you may experience diminished desire for food. You may not look forward to eating with the same enjoyment. Even highly spiced food may seem bland and uninteresting. As the depression increases, you may miss a meal and not realize it because your appetite is gone. At the most severe level, you may have to force yourself to eat (sometimes even be forced to eat). A return of appetite may signal that the depression is lifting.

Then again, you may believe that eating is the solution. Although it may seem strange, overeating is similar to undereating as a symptom, in that food consumption is affected by mood. Food may not give any enjoyment. You may not taste food or enjoy the subtle flavors of well-prepared meals. In this situation, you just eat—and eat and eat and eat. You may sometimes tell yourself that you deserve to eat because everything else in your life stinks. If you ask yourself if you are really enjoying the food, your answer may be no.

Diet and nutrition can have a significant influence on depression. When the BEAST is in charge, you may make very poor food choices. You may consume an overabundance of sugar and not enough protein. Although a quart (or gallon) of double-mocha fudge ice cream may seem to be just what the doctor ordered, eating that much can make you more depressed ("Look at me, sitting here gorging myself"), and the aftermath can strengthen the BEAST ("I can't believe it: I've gained 10 pounds in the past month").

The high sugar intake may also cause a quick drop of blood sugar later on, with the accompanying feeling of being down. With a low energy level, you may not fix healthy meals and instead end up with junk food. A diet of cookies, potato chips, soda, and ice cream may be easy and available, but it is a nutritional disaster for you and a gourmet feast for the BEAST. Many people skip meals as a result of rushing, minimizing the importance of food, or attempting an ill-advised form of diet. Without fuel, the body becomes depleted physically and emotionally.

Your first exercise in this section is to report what you ate yesterday and when.

Morning meal (time of day):
Snack(s) (time of day):
Midday meal (time of day):
Snack(s) (time of day):
Evening meal (time of day):
Snack(s) (time of day):

A poor diet has specific effects. Too little protein can affect energy levels. Too much sugar can lead to a rapid rise and subsequent drops in activity and concentration. Not eating fiber can affect regularity, which can also have an impact on your mood.

Note in the brief survey of your food intake yesterday whether any of the following statements is true.

	Untrue	Somewhat True	Very True
1. You are skipping meals.			
2. There is little protein and an abundance of sweets in your diet.			
3. Few, if any, fiber-rich foods (fruits, vegetables, and grains) are in your diet.			
4. The number of calories in your diet is extremely high or low.			

If any of your responses to the survey is very true, then it may be time to adjust your diet. Experiment with a better diet for a week. Keep a diary of what you eat, along with monitoring your mood. In this way, you can more easily determine whether changing your diet may enhance your mood.

Certain kinds of food may alleviate some symptoms of depression. L-tryptophan, an amino acid, is said to be associated with better sleep patterns. It is metabolized into melatonin. Taking any over-the-counter version of these compounds is not recommended unless you are supervised by a medical doctor, but certain common foods have L-tryptophan in them and are perfectly safe. Milk, broccoli, and turkey all contain high quantities of this chemical and may promote better sleep when you eat them regularly.

And then there are foods that are dangerous to your sleep. Coffee, colas, chocolate, tea, and other beverages that have caffeine will make getting to sleep more difficult if you indulge a few hours before bedtime. Eating harder-to-digest foods such as red meats and proteins can keep you from getting to sleep as well. Better dinnertime choices are complex carbohydrates (like pasta, potatoes, and breads) and less animal protein. If you do not eat at regular times and have a diet without a balance of protein, carbohydrates, fiber, fresh fruit, and vegetables, you may be contributing to mood problems. Although a better diet is not usually the only solution to a better mood, it is important to your overall well-being.

Mood and Sleep

Sleep difficulty is one of the major symptoms of depression. Studies have shown that individuals who are depressed have not only greater trouble falling asleep but also greater difficulty staying asleep. Your sleep may be very restless, and you may wake up earlier than you would like, feeling exhausted. This fatigue can affect your work and lead to daytime naps. The net result is a cycle of sleep difficulty in which you sleep during the day to compensate for your inability to sleep the night before, and then you are not able to fall asleep at night.

The BEAST may rob you of sleep.

Or make you feel so tired that you can hardly get out of bed.

Mood and Energy Loss

When the BEAST is upon you, it saps your energy.

Your energy level may shift during the day. You might wake up feeling energetic and back to your old self, only to feel your energy slip away throughout the day, or you may wake up feeling tired and then gain energy during the day. Some individuals who are depressed wake up fatigued, go to sleep fatigued, and then have trouble sleeping. One symptom of depression is a lack of energy to do anything. When you are depressed, you may feel as though you have run a 20-mile race without having moved a muscle. It is often a problem of inertia, which may feel like being stuck to the ground. Have you ever tried to push a heavy object such as a chair or appliance? What is the hardest part? Usually, it is getting the object moving or breaking through inertia. Once the object is in motion, it is easier to move. You start to build momentum, and that momentum contributes to the ease of motion. Doing the exercises in this program will help you break through inertia and build up momentum for change.

Mood and Loss of Sexual Interest

For some people, depression involves a loss of interest in sex, diminished sex drive, or an overall loss of interest in other people. If you are mildly depressed, there might be a slight loss of sexual interest or lowered responsiveness to sexual stimuli. As depression increases, you might become sexually interested or aroused only with considerable stimulation. If you are severely depressed, you may have an aversion to sex.

How Health Problems Affect Depression

Both physical and biochemical factors can be related to affect. Misinterpretation of physical problems may lead to emotional difficulties, and sometimes remedying a medical ailment can lead to improved mood. For example, Kristen "felt" she could not get out of bed, even though she woke up earlier than she had planned. Her body ached, she was tired, and her stomach felt so bad she thought she would never want to see solid food again. It was difficult for her to concentrate on anything; when she tried, her head ached.

Kristen is definitely ailing. Is it a mood problem? It could be. She experienced early morning awakening, fatigue, muscle tension, and concentration problems. However, these problems could also be symptoms of the flu or some other physical malady. If it is the flu, improvement may not seem to come fast enough, but the probability is that Kristen will feel better in a few days if she gets rest, drinks liquids, and does not overexert herself.

One of the first steps in treatment to relieve depression is to find out if depressive symptoms are being caused by medical problems. If you have not seen a physician in a long time (over a year is considered a long time), you should get a checkup, whether or not you think you may be depressed. Many treatable medical difficulties masquerade as depression, and physical problems involving pain (like headaches and stomachaches), muscle tension (muscle strain, cramps, and so on), and discomfort with internal organs should first be checked out by a medical doctor. If disease or other physical malady is ruled out, you may then proceed with the methods of cognitive therapy.

Here is a partial list of symptoms to review. If any of these symptoms are pronounced, go to your doctor and get them checked before assuming that you have only a mood problem.

1. Sleep difficulties
   a. Frequent wakening
   b. Inability to fall asleep
   c. Sleeping more than 10 hours a night
2. Stomach/digestive problems
   a. Constipation/diarrhea
   b. Frequent nausea/vomiting
   c. Inability to eat solid foods
3. Muscle/skeletal symptoms
   a. Muscle/tendon/joint pain
   b. Knotting or constant cramping
   c. Constant fatigue
   d. Frequent or lengthy episodes of headache

How Genetics Affect Mood

Another aspect of the physical dimension of depression is genetics. Do some people inherit a tendency to be depressed? Although the answer is probably, no matter how a person becomes depressed, the methods to improve mood described in this program can be effective. The scientific pursuit to find a genetic code may eventually support genetic predisposition as one factor in developing mood problems. However, the influence of genetics cannot be studied in isolation because genetic and environmental influences are so interrelated. Parents may pass on a genetic code for low mood and negative thinking. They also influence thinking, situations, and actions in their children by their parenting skills and the behavior they model. Modeling is essentially setting an example. As a child, your most significant influences for how to be in the world are your parents. As you read this page, you may be way ahead, considering how your mother or father affected you and your actions and emotions. But where did they get their attitudes and beliefs? Just a genetic explanation is probably insufficient in most cases.

Most studies done on mood and genetics require isolating factors. For example, studying identical twins who were raised apart allows more control over the nature-nurture debate. People who live in a culture that is contained and receives little influence from outside environments have also been the target of research in this area.

There is no specific test or method we can give you to determine whether genetic inheritance is a factor that affects your mood difficulties. But what if it did? You are still faced with the same options about what to do next. History and genetics cannot be changed. This program asks you to ponder the present and make changes for a better future for yourself.

1. True or false: My parents and grandparents had problems with depression. That means I will have problems, too. (False. There is no test to tell if your mood problems are inherited.)
2. True or false: If I have a genetic predisposition for depression, I can get my genes altered. (False. No methods exist to alter your genes, unless you are talking about Levi's jeans.)
3. True or false: If I eat right, I can probably improve my mood. (True. A good diet can help your mood.)
4. True or false: If I don't get at least 8 hours of sleep a night, I will get depressed. (False. Sleep is different for different individuals. Lack of sleep can be a symptom of depression, but sleep alone is not a determining factor.)
5. True or false: Being in good physical condition will enhance my effort to improve my mood. (True. Keeping your body healthy can influence your self-esteem and how you feel.)

Bodies, Chemistry, Medication, and Depression

Medications may be effective for depression by interacting with the physical aspects of this condition. You have learned that when you have a headache, aspirin (or some similar medication) is effective, safe, and inexpensive. Similarly, medications for depression have been shown to be very effective in alleviating many symptoms relatively rapidly (often between 1 and 3 weeks).

Although people have little difficulty taking drugs for problems such as hypertension, headaches, and infections, among many other *physical* afflictions, the idea of taking pills to improve their mood is uncomfortable for some individuals. For those who view depression as purely psychological, medication is often seen as a cop-out. Some people think medicine is a crutch for a problem that should be solved only with willpower; some mental health professionals also have a negative view of the use of medications for treatment of mood disorders. Other people fear developing a dependency on the pills.

Large volumes of research support the effectiveness of medical treatment in combination with psychotherapy (Wright, 1987). Drug treatments may allow people to mobilize themselves in therapy to learn ways to change their thinking and behavior, a sort of kick start. New medications are safer and have fewer side effects than those used in the pioneer days of psychopharmacology. In the most severe cases of depression, antidepressant drugs may be lifesaving. In milder cases, medication is worth considering after you gain an understanding of what the drugs actually do or do not do.

The biochemistry—and specifically the neurochemistry—in your body is always a component of emotion but not the only part of what you experience with depression. Antidepressants lift depression for many people through complex biological changes having to do with the transmission of impulses through the nervous system. Rather than relying on medication alone, you can increase your resources by combining medication and therapy. You can also change your neurochemistry when you change patterns of thinking and acting.

Treating Depression with Medication

This section describes specific ways that medication interacts with the body to improve affect. It includes technical terms that you may want to ask your therapist to explain.

Information travels around your body on an extensive network of nerve cells called *neurons*. These neurons have a large bulb at one end and a long stem coming from the bulb. Messages in the form of electrical impulses move from one neuron to the next by the chemicals that the neurons transmit (e.g., serotonin). When neuron number one releases the neurotransmitters, they flood the space between neuron one and neuron two. When neuron two receives this stimulation, it is triggered to carry the message to neuron three, and so on down the line. A large percentage of the neurotransmitter substance (e.g., serotonin) then returns to the bulb at the end of the transmitting neuron in a process called *reuptake*. The leftover amounts are broken down into other substances by an enzyme called *monoamine oxidase*. Some antidepressants work to block reuptake, but others block the enzyme monoamine oxidase from breaking down the transmitters. With these types of medications, the desired result is that more neurotransmitters remain, which enables more transmissions to occur between neurons. This change helps promote a better mood.

How Fast Does It Work?

When starting antidepressant medication, you need to know that the results are not experienced immediately. Unlike aspirin and other pain medications, which provide relief from symptoms in less than an hour, antidepressants take 2 to 3 weeks to build up to a therapeutic level in the body and must be taken daily as prescribed. The full effect desired may take 3 months or more to achieve. In the first few days or weeks, there may be some signs of improvement, but during this time the side effects are more likely to be noticed as well.

Side Effects

Most people experience some side effects when they take antidepressants. Not all of them may be bad, and many individuals notice no side effects at all. However, you need to be prepared for this possibility if you start a medical treatment. Every individual is different, and some classes or subclasses of these types of drugs are better suited for some people and not for others. The most important criterion for a good match of medication to individual is the main effect, improvement of mood and related bodily functioning, and you need to be patient with the potential secondary effects. Do not end your efforts with medication before you give it a chance to take effect because of the initial discomfort of side effects that may lessen over time. If you take an antidepressant, be sure to check with your physician if you experience secondary effects. These side effects are often easily accommodated. For example, dry mouth can be dealt with by chewing gum or drinking more fluids. For many people, the body does the accommodation without much help.

It is essential that a physician who is well versed in the use of psychotherapeutic drugs closely monitors your medication. Typically, medication for mood is administered initially in a lower than therapeutic dose to decrease the possibility of uncomfortable side effects as you slowly build up the level of the medication in your body. Once you are able to tolerate the first few days of medication, your physician (usually a psychiatrist) begins to increase the amount to get to a range that will ensure a main effect. The drug level in your bloodstream can be measured in the plasma of your blood. The suggested therapeutic dosage and actual blood plasma range vary. Both are monitored to ensure that you have the proper amount of medication to help you improve your mood. Because most people's metabolic systems are different, individual attention to dosage is crucial. For this reason, *never* take a friend or family member's antidepressant drugs.

If you are taking antidepressants, it is imperative that you follow the dosage recommended by your doctor and *do not experiment* with dosages on your own. Some people are tempted to stop their medication once they start to feel better. The temptation to discontinue, if followed, may lead to a rebound effect, and you may experience a rapid decline in mood. Please do not take such risks. Collaborate with your therapist and physician before making any sudden changes.

Alcohol and Antidepressants

Alcohol and antidepressant medication should not be mixed. Alcohol interferes with the activity of antidepressants. Drinking not only can preempt the effects of medication but also can aggravate your mood problems by interfering with your medication's effects on neurotransmission. Wines and some foods can cause great difficulty with certain types of antidepressants. Your medical doctor is the best source of information regarding diet and drugs, but you are the one who must use the information wisely in your daily life.

Deciding About Medication

As we have said in other parts of this workbook, depression is not explained by a simple cause-and-effect relationship between biology and mood. Although medication may be extremely helpful for many people, it is not always necessary. Whether to use medication should be an informed decision that involves careful discussion with your physician. If your symptoms are very severe, listen to what your doctor says before ruling out the use of drugs in your treatment. If your symptoms are not moderate to severe, medication may not be what you need. Remember, these drugs are not without side effects.

Chapter 3 Review

1. Name two physical symptoms that are related to depression.

2. How does depression affect eating habits? How has depression affected your eating habits?

3. How does depression affect sleep? How has it affected your sleep?

4. What part do genetics play in depression? Is there a history of depression in your family?

5. Name some ways that medications can work to affect mood.

Understanding the Impact of Emotion: The E of the BEAST

The goals of this chapter are

- to understand the differences between thoughts and feelings
- to identify the symptoms of depression related to emotion
- to evaluate your level of depression
- to understand emotion and the role it plays in depression
- to understand self-compassion

Differences between Thoughts and Feelings

One of the most common phrases in our language is "I feel. . . ." Too often, thoughts are confused with emotions or feelings. Both are so important that they are worth looking at separately. If you try to combine them, you see neither your feelings nor your thoughts clearly. To illustrate this point, try the following exercise. Identify each of these statements as either a thought or a feeling.

	Thought	Feeling
1. I feel like things will never get any better.	○	○
2. I feel like a loser.	○	○
3. I feel depressed.	○	○
4. I feel as if you don't love me.	○	○
5. I feel sorry for you.	○	○

	Thought	Feeling
6. I feel angry.	○	○
7. I feel confused.	○	○
8. I feel calm.	○	○
9. I feel like a fifth wheel.	○	○
10. I feel unloved.	○	○

If you identified any statements other than numbers 3 and 6 as feelings, please read the following section very carefully. All of the other statements are thoughts. The fact that you use the phrase "I feel" does not necessarily make these statements feelings. In fact, by seeing them as feelings, you obscure the real feelings that are related to those thoughts. For example, if you say to yourself or others, "I *think* that I'm a fifth wheel," you can identify how that makes you *feel,* perhaps "I feel lonely." Let's take a closer look at how emotions and thoughts relate to each other.

Imagine this situation: You are at home at night. You are in bed and about to go to sleep. The lights are out, you have gotten too tired to read or watch TV and you feel comfortable with your head on the pillow and the covers over you. You then hear some noise at the window.

Here are two different examples of "cognitions" or thoughts involving interpretations. Read them and fill in the answers to the questions that follow.

Interpretation: When you hear the noise, you think, "There's a noise at the window. Someone is out there trying to break into the house. They want to rob me. If they get in, they might murder me! I would be helpless to do anything about it."

1. How would your body react to this interpretation of the situation? Would you feel relaxed and comfortable?

2. In a word or two, what would your emotions be with this interpretation?

3. How would you react to this interpretation? What would you do?

Alternative Interpretation: Look at the same situation with a different interpretation of the noise: "There's a noise at the window. The weatherman said there would be wind and rain tonight. I'm glad I kept the windows closed. I love the sound of the wind and rain blowing against the window. It's so relaxing, and the grass and flowers sure need the water."

1. How would your body react to this interpretation of the situation? Would you feel relaxed and comfortable?

2. In a word or two, what would your accompanying emotions be with this interpretation?

3. How would you react to this interpretation? What would you do?

This exercise illustrates the fact that the same situation interpreted in different ways may be associated with entirely different emotions and subsequent actions. Interpretation 1 might lead to fear and anxiety. However, you would probably feel calm and relaxed if you had made the alternative interpretation. In this case, your behavior would probably allow you to fall asleep.

From this exercise, you can see that situation, thoughts, and emotions balance each other in the complex system by which you experience events. Consider what you experience with depression.

The Importance of Feelings

When you are depressed, it is not a good idea to trust your feelings as the basis for making decisions. Although feelings are valuable in most life experiences, they may sustain your misery when you are depressed. You may "feel" so bad that you do not enjoy doing anything. You may avoid others, eat poorly, and begin to hate yourself. These symptom-based decisions may maintain your depression if left unexamined. To get control over depression, you must work with your therapist to make decisions that are consistent with overcoming your depression, rather than decisions that are driven by your negative feelings.

The ABCs of Emotion

Albert Ellis, one of the pioneers of cognitive therapy, developed a model to explain how feelings are connected to other factors in your life. This model is known as the ABCs of emotion (Ellis & Harper, 1961).

Activating Event	Belief	Consequences
A	B	C

Between the circumstances that lead to a change in your mood (A, activating event) and the emotional results (C, consequences), you make an interpretation based on your beliefs (B). By becoming aware of your biased, irrational beliefs and the distressing emotional fallout that is the consequence of those beliefs, you can begin to understand them and then change.

For example, Sally has been sad for days because she thought she failed a test in school. Sally has a very high grade point average and has seldom performed poorly on tests. However, Sally continued to worry and imagined herself flunking the course and eventually having to quit school because of her grades. Unfortunately, after almost every exam she took, she experienced this period of sadness and worry with similar thoughts about her future. The activating event (A) was waiting for the results of the exam she completed. The consequence (C) was sadness and worry. What would you guess was the belief (B) associated with the activating event and consequence (see choices below)?

1. I should always make an A on my tests.
2. Tomorrow is another day.
3. I am not smart enough to get through school.
4. My parents do not give me enough support to help me do well in school.

If you chose 3, you were correct. Sally maintains a belief about herself that makes it hard for her to feel confident about her efforts. She has so much self-doubt that it seems to override her perspective on overall performance, past efforts, and positive sense of the future. Instead, she feels sad and worried, in large part because of an unreasonable belief (B).

Many people get stuck by trying to pin problems on just one global factor. The situation may be part of the problem, but it is rarely the only explanation. There are external and internal factors that affect you, and in this program you will consider how you and the situation interact. People who are feeling depressed may try to find the "core" reason for their emotional pain. Most of the time, they wind up frustrated and feeling worse. It is much more productive to search for and change several different factors to improve mood than to seek the elusive key to release you from all problems. Being able to turn off emotional distress like a faucet is nice to imagine, but the world around you, your thoughts, and your biochemistry all interact and affect your ability to gain control over depression. Making some desirable changes in any of the interacting factors is an attainable goal.

Self-Compassion as an Aid to Emotion

Self-compassion means having mercy on yourself and giving yourself a break when you make a mistake. All of those old clichés are true. Everyone is human; we all make mistakes. The first step in becoming compassionate toward yourself is recognizing that you will continue to make mistakes. When people are depressed, they are more likely to be self-critical. Under the oppression of such self-criticism, the potential for constructive change is lessened.

Perhaps there is another aspect to this problem. People who grow up in a critical environment accommodate in various ways. One way is to depend on criticism for external motivation and to know what changes to make. People who adapt this way may become more self-critical and depend on this attitude to push themselves. It is possible to cultivate more compassion toward yourself and to change your maladaptive patterns, even deeply ingrained ones, but it takes specific kinds of effort. To help you toward this goal, ask yourself these questions.

- When I am self-critical, do my criticisms sound like those I heard while I was growing up? If so, I can understand that this pattern was learned and can now teach myself differently.

- How would I evaluate my efforts, skill development, and judgment in this situation? Be specific.

- What would I do if confronted with this situation again, taking all I can from this experience? Be specific.

- How would I feel toward someone else I care about who was in the same circumstance?

You can learn to give yourself the same room to be human that you give to others. Remember, you cannot redo the past, but you can think of each experience as an opportunity to learn. You can anticipate similar situations in the future and avoid making the same mistakes.

All of this is designed to help you improve your emotions and mood. That also means that you need to be reasonable in how you evaluate your own progress. Along the way you are going to make mistakes, and you will probably catch many of them. What you do when you realize each mistake is important. You can deal constructively with the situation by realistically evaluating your part in it rather than getting stuck in a cycle of self-criticism and blame. One of the central goals of this program is enabling you to approach your problems in a more positive fashion.

To begin this process, you can review points in this chapter by answering the following questions:

1. What are your general complaints?

2. What are the primary specific problems?

3. How do these problems affect you?

4. Take this initial problem list and develop a more detailed and specific exhaustive problem list.

5. How do you explain these problems to yourself?

6. How do you see these problems in relation to your depression?

7. What is your assumed general explanation for their cause?

8. How do you relate these problems to your depression, and what are your expectations about the outcome?

9. What evidence is there for your explanations or theories?

10. What alternative explanations, other than the ones you hold, might account for these connections?

11. How might the interaction of your thoughts, behavior, and life events result in depression?

12. How are your thoughts, behaviors, and the environment maintaining your depression?

13. How did you come to think and behave the way you do?

14. How would these ideas explain current and past events?

15. What predictions could be made about the ways your schemas and automatic thoughts will affect your feelings and behavior within and outside therapy?

16. What would be the evidence?

You and your therapist (and friends and family) may have different explanations for your depression. The goal is not to convince other people of the correctness of your explanation but to see your explanation as a theory about yourself, the world, and your future. Theories of depression can be assessed with information and experience, and they can be revised when necessary. The aim is to help you distance yourself from your theory so that you can evaluate it.

Chapter 4 Review

1. True or false: Self-compassion is simply feeling sorry for yourself.

2. Is there a single event, fact, or insight that will totally change all of your feelings?

3. What do the ABCs of emotion stand for, and how can you use them to change what you feel?

Taking Action: The A of the BEAST

The goals of this chapter are

- to understand the importance of taking action to recover from depression
- to identify activities and environments that are pleasurable
- to break the habit of procrastination
- to learn methods for improving your mood by engaging in new activities

So far, this program has described depression and explained why doing something about your depression is important. This chapter begins to highlight several techniques for activities that are antidepressive.

Why Make the Effort?

As discussed in previous chapters, inertia is stagnation, which can lead to a lowering of mood. Action physically affects symptoms of low mood by potentially activating a sense of well-being. For example, how do you feel after exercise, like a brisk walk or jog? Most people feel some relief, and others experience a genuine, but temporary, improvement in mood. There are also neurochemical shifts, brain changes, and general physical activation that combat the lack of motivation associated with depression. Because moods are temporary, activities that help to improve mood must be repeated to sustain the effect. Your first step is trying activities and breaking the pattern of inertia ("an object at rest tends to remain at rest").

An easy way to begin to look at the way your behaviors and level of activity are related to your mood is to use an activity schedule. The activity schedule is a very important tool for your therapy program, so take the time and make the effort to understand it well.

Using the Activity Schedule

Figure 5.1 is a blank activity schedule for you to photocopy. The days of the week are across the top, and the hours of the day are on the side. Keep a record of your activities daily and by the hour as illustrated in Figure 5.2. Do not let the simplicity of this method of observing and monitoring yourself fool you into thinking it will not have an impact on your efforts to change. This method will take you about 5 minutes a day. The sooner you record your data, the more reliable the information will be. (Remember the recency effect?) There are many useful purposes for this activity.

1. Your first few activity records will provide a baseline or record of how much activity you were involved in when you started this program. They will establish a starting point in your efforts to improve your life. If you are to find out if this program works, you will need to see how you were doing when you started as compared to how you are doing as you practice the self-enhancement assignments.
2. By observing your activities and how you feel when you participate in these activities, you can find out how often you feel down and what situations are associated with feeling more or less emotionally distressed. Along with your activities, write down what you were feeling while you engaged in the activity. Rating the sense of mastery and pleasure you felt during this activity will be discussed below.
3. By filling in a box for each hour of the day, you can examine specifically what is happening in your daily life and how your activities are related to your mood. You will be writing a notation in each box about what you were doing (actions) during each hour. You can write in a few words that remind you of the event that occurred. The more activities you record, the more useful this task is likely to be for you. Take care to avoid labeling large blocks of time as "sitting," "in bed," "watching TV," or "doing nothing." Even while watching TV, you are probably involved in other behaviors.

Once you have recorded your first activity schedule, you will have begun accomplishing several goals. You will be able to

1. assess your present use of time
2. plan better and more productive use of your time to attack depression and hopelessness
3. start to get into the idea of doing self-enhancement assignments
4. begin to test the ideas you may have that you are doing nothing

Note: Grade activities for Mastery (M) and Pleasure (P) on a scale from 0–10

	Monday	M	P	Tuesday	M	P	Wednesday	M	P	Thursday	M	P	Friday	M	P	Saturday	M	P	Sunday	M	P
6–8 am																					
8–10 am																					
10 am–12 pm																					
12–2 pm																					
2–4 pm																					
4–6 pm																					
6–8 pm																					
8–10 pm																					
10 pm–12 am																					
12–6 am																					

Figure 5.1. **Activity Schedule** **Week # ______ Date: ____________**

Note: Grade activities for Mastery (M) and Pleasure (P) on a scale from 0–10

	Monday	M	P	Tuesday	M	P	Wednesday	M	P	Thursday	M	P	Friday	M	P	Saturday	M	P	Sunday	M	P
6–8 am	Get up Eat breakfast	1 3	2 1	Get up Eat breakfast	3 1	2 1	Get up Eat breakfast	1 3	2 3	Get up Eat breakfast	1 3	2 1	Get up Eat breakfast	3 1	2 3	Sleep	2	1	Sleep	3	2
8–10 am	Go to work	2	3	Go to work	2	3	Go to work	2	1	Go to work	2	3	Go to work	2	1	Go on a walk	1	2	Take a swim	1	3
10 am–12 pm	Work on new project	1	2	Meet with client	3	2	Give presentation	1	2	Collect research at library	3	2	Work on new project	1	2	Go to brunch with friends	3	3	Read the newspaper	2	1
12–2 pm	Go to lunch	3	1	Go to lunch	1	3	Go to lunch	3	1	Go to lunch	1	3	Go to lunch	3	1	"Weed" the garden	2	1	Meet parents for lunch	1	2
2–4 pm	Finish old project	2	3	Training seminar	2	1	Meet with supervisor	2	3	Write proposal	2	1	Work on new project	2	3	Take a nap	1	2	Take a nap	3	3
4–6 pm	Go home Eat dinner	4 1	5 2	Go home Eat dinner	1 3	2 4	Go home Eat dinner	3 1	2 1	Go home Eat dinner	1 3	2 1	Go home Eat dinner	3 1	2 3	Shower and get ready	3	1	Walk the dog	2	1
6–8 pm	Clean house	3	4	Wash dog	3	2	Go shopping at the mall	2	3	Go to the gym	2	3	Go grocery shopping	2	1	Meet friends for dinner	2	3	Eat dinner	1	2
8–10 pm	Watch TV Read	5 2	1 3	Go out with friend	1	3	Take hot bubble bath	4	5	Watch TV Read	1 3	2 4	Meet with book club	1	2	Watch TV	3	2	Read Watch TV	3 5	4 1
10 pm–12 am	Get ready for bed	4	5	Get ready for bed	2	1	Get ready for bed	4	3	Get ready for bed	4	3	Get ready for bed	3	1	Get ready for bed	1	3	Get ready for bed	2	3
12–6 am	Sleep	3	4	Sleep	3	2	Sleep	3	4	Sleep	2	1	Sleep	2	3	Sleep	1	2	Sleep	5	4

Figure 5.2. Example Activity Schedule **Week # 1 Date: 6/29/98**

Common self-statements for many people include "There aren't enough hours in the day to do all that I need to do" and "I never get anything done." If you are feeling overloaded and unable to cope with what you see as overwhelming demands, you may not be coping with your perceived load by scheduling time to do what needs to be done. Scheduling usually requires planning an hour, a day, or a week in advance. The goal of activity scheduling is to maximize your potential for productivity by making more effective use of the available time.

Recording Your Sense of Mastery and Pleasure in Activities

Another important part of monitoring your activity is to start to evaluate not only what you do but also how much of a sense of mastery and how much pleasure you experience with these activities. As you can see, the instructions at the top of the activity schedule tell you to fill out each hour with the activity you are involved in and then rate it for mastery and pleasure on a scale of 0 to 10. *Mastery* is your ability to perform the activity. A score of 10 would indicate you are performing a task with exceptional skill; a score of 0 would mean you barely know what you are doing and sense you are accomplishing nothing in spite of your efforts. *Pleasure* is your sense of satisfaction with the task or activity described. A score of 10 would mean that you are having more fun and enjoyment than at almost any previous time in your life. A pleasure rating of 0 would indicate misery and unhappiness. An enduring sense of pleasure or mastery is not usually present at the same time as depression. Therefore, by monitoring these experiences, you can more accurately assess mood fluctuation throughout the day.

Once again, remember the recency and primacy effects; we tend to report the things that just happened and the things that occurred first in a sequence more accurately than other events that we experience. Try to fill out the activity schedule at the end of each day or in the morning and in the evening. The longer you delay, the less accurate your memory will be.

Figure 5.2 is an example of how the activity schedule is completed. Remember, for each activity you will be judging your experience of mastery and pleasure. One measure does not always affect the other. For example, if you are doing the dishes, you may have a particular method for getting them squeaky clean. You have mastered the art of dishwashing at a world-class level, so give yourself a mastery level of 9 or 10. However, you get no enjoyment from doing this job except relief from finishing the task. The pleasure rating would be a 4.

Of course, there is no way to check your ratings for absolute accuracy. They are subjective. You may find that the situations you track on the activity schedule will vary in how you experience events emotionally (pleasure) and by evaluation (mastery). One way to adjust your system to be consistent is to look at anything above the rating of 5 as above average for mastery or pleasure. A 10 would be the best you have ever experienced, and a 0 would represent the worst ever encountered.

Let's take another example. You are learning to use a computer. You still have not figured out the difference between a hard drive and a hard-to-understand manual, but you have enjoyed the process of playing with your new "toy." Your mastery rating may be a 1. Because you are having fun exploring the computer, however, it is possible that your pleasure rating could be a 7, even if you hardly know what you are doing.

- Name an activity that gives you pleasure but that you have little skill (mastery) in performing.

- Now, list an activity you have mastery in but from which you derive little pleasure.

- Next, list an activity in which you have little mastery and little pleasure.

- Finally, name an activity for which you experience high levels of both mastery and pleasure.

The reason for recording your mastery and pleasure of activities is to make an effort to observe in a much more systematic manner how your mood varies. If asked how often low mood is experienced, many individuals who are depressed say, "All the time" and perhaps not realize that the mood was associated with a low-pleasure activity. This reported experience is probably influenced by the primacy and recency effects. If you say you are depressed all or most of the time, you are operating from an untested theory about yourself that does not take situational factors into account. If you accept theory as fact, without examination of evidence to test a theory, you could be sustaining a belief that will keep you depressed. If you examine factors such as pleasure derived from your activities, you come to a better understanding of the controllable factors that contribute to your depression.

Testing Theory with Observation

In addition to using the activity schedule to learn more about daily mood patterns, you can test your theory by counting the total number of squares filled in on your activity schedule once you finish the week. This number represents 100% or the total. Then count the number of squares, first, where the pleasure rating is 5 or above and, second, where the mastery rating is 5 or above. On a calculator, divide the high-pleasure number by the total and get a percentage for pleasure. Do the same for mastery. Remember, before you actually collect the information over a given week, you have only an untested theory of the result.

What is your theory about how much of your activity will rate above 5 for mastery?

Before	**After**
☐ _____ None	Actual result _____
☐ _____ Less than 25%	
☐ _____ Less than 50%	
☐ _____ Less than 75%	
☐ _____ All	

What is your best guess about the percentage of activity that will rate above 5 for pleasure?

Before	**After**
☐ _____ None	Actual result _____
☐ _____ Less than 25%	
☐ _____ Less than 50%	
☐ _____ Less than 75%	
☐ _____ All	

If you have underestimated the amount of pleasure you experience in a week's time, you could have a tendency to go with the primacy and recency effects when you experience low mood. If you overestimated the amount of pleasure you derive from your experiences of the week, you may have a core of optimism that you will want to work on keeping. If you were right about mastery and pleasure ratings in advance of your efforts to collect the information on yourself, your understanding of your mood patterns and activity seems accurate.

The information from your activity schedule efforts will be valuable in a variety of ways. If the accuracy of your prediction was way off, then you may have a negatively or positively biased view of the future that is worth looking at more carefully. Also, no matter how accurate your prediction was, the observations in your personal activity schedule will give you important information to work with in this program.

Identifying Patterns Associated with Low Mood

You will begin to identify recurring events or associations of events that you may not have been aware of before you began recording your activities.

1. *Patterns of low mood.* Were there any recurring situations or events that were associated with feeling bad?

	Time	Recurring Event
Monday	________	________
Tuesday	________	________
Wednesday	________	________
Thursday	________	________
Friday	________	________
Saturday	________	________
Sunday	________	________

2. *Environment associated with low mood.* Were there any places that seemed to be connected to being depressed? Were there places where you felt better?

	Place	Mood
Monday	________	________
Tuesday	________	________
Wednesday	________	________
Thursday	________	________
Friday	________	________
Saturday	________	________
Sunday	________	________

3. *People and mood.* Was your mood likely to be better or worse around certain people?

	Person	**Mood**
Monday	________________	______________________
Tuesday	________________	______________________
Wednesday	________________	______________________
Thursday	________________	______________________
Friday	________________	______________________
Saturday	________________	______________________
Sunday	________________	______________________

4. *Activities.* Were there certain things that you did that seemed to be related to fluctuation in your mood?

	Activity	**Mood**
Monday	________________	______________________
Tuesday	________________	______________________
Wednesday	________________	______________________
Thursday	________________	______________________
Friday	________________	______________________
Saturday	________________	______________________
Sunday	________________	______________________

Making the Effort to Change: Why Do Today What I Can Put Off Until Tomorrow?

A common characteristic of people who are depressed is their lack of goal-directed activity, maintained by a tendency to procrastinate. Ask yourself this question: Am I engaging in activities with the same frequency that I used to? If the answer is no, your activity level is down.

How many times have you promised yourself or others that as soon as you are less depressed you will get around to it (a round TUIT)? This is procrastination. We have created the TUIT button to remind you that now may be the best time to do the activities that you have been putting off.

Everyone has reasons for not doing today what they can do tomorrow. A problem develops when many of the things that you usually do are put off. A significant

decrease in activities has many effects on you. At first glance, you may appear to be avoiding criticism or failure. You may even think that you are avoiding activities that do not really matter or that you cannot possibly complete. Avoiding activities leads only to more avoidance, and lack of activity will delay your recovery from depression.

In the early 1980s, a famous artificial heart transplant operation was performed. A man named Barney needed a new heart, or he was going to die. A human heart was not available, so a mechanical one was used to help him survive until a biological heart became available. Barney survived the surgery and was in good spirits when he was initially in recovery. Two days after the operation, he had a sip of beer and a conversation with President Ronald Reagan on the telephone. He said he was glad to be alive. But as the weeks went by, he started to become depressed.

What do you think the doctors and nurses did to help Barney with his depression? They did not give him antidepressants because they were concerned about how antidepressants might interact with the medicines he was taking to keep him from rejecting the heart. They may have tried to get him to "think positively," but that was not the most effective intervention. Barney's mood improved when he got up on a walking device with his artificial heart motor in tow. He walked laps around the hospital floor. Movement—going from inactivity to some type of action—helped to improve Barney's mood. Action can promote a significant change in mood. Interrupting the inactivity of depression is a powerful way to start treatment.

Increased action can promote a chemical change in the body that improves mood. Have you ever felt so down that you wanted to stay home or even in bed all day? If you did stay put, did it help you feel better? Probably not. One of the things we work with in therapy is how you *act*.

Two exercises follow that can help you understand and improve your low activity level. The first is a series of questions about what you've been doing recently. The second is a diary of the basic activities of your day.

Exercise 1

1. Are you spending more time in bed each day than you used to?
2. Have you stopped doing enjoyable things with your family?
3. Have you stopped doing enjoyable things with your friends?
4. Do things that used to be pleasant for you now fall flat?
5. Do you find yourself waiting for the "perfect" time to do something?
6. Do you find yourself starting projects but not completing them?
7. Do you say to yourself, "It doesn't really matter" more often?
8. Do you find yourself just too busy to do the things that you need to?
9. Do you find yourself "forgetting" more often than you used to?
10. Is being a procrastinator a good excuse for not doing anything?
11. Is your work receiving more criticism than it used to?
12. Have you been taking less time on your appearance lately?

All of these questions point to a diminished activity level and a lack of pleasure from previously enjoyed activities. The BEAST of depression is maintained by lack of activity. The lack of activity drains you, and depression is the result.

Now that you have examined your activities and the ways that your activities may be systematically related to your moods, you can begin to use this information. By planning each day ahead of time, you become an active agent in planning your life. You may now use your knowledge about how your activities affect your mood in scheduling. Fill out the planning schedule (Figure 5.3). After you have planned your day's activities, you should set your plan aside and go about your day. At the end of the day when you review your activity schedule, you will see which activities you actually engaged in and how much pleasure (P) you experienced during the activity. You will be using the planning schedule and the activity schedule throughout the program. If you photocopy both forms now, you will always have blank copies available. This process of active planning and then monitoring the patterns of your activities and moods will help you overcome depression and lower your risk of relapse. Your therapist can be an active partner in helping you identify and understand these patterns.

Month:

Monday, Date: ___________	Thursday, Date: ___________
Tuesday, Date: ___________	Friday, Date: ___________
Wednesday, Date: ___________	Saturday, Date: ___________
	Sunday, Date: ___________

Figure 5.3. **Planning Schedule**

Recovering Lost Activity

Have you ever asked yourself, "Why did I stop doing that?" when you see someone engaged in an activity you once enjoyed? People often ask that question even when they are not having serious problems with low mood. Now that you have worked through some of your low mood issues and are addressing them head on, perhaps it is time to think back and ask yourself that question about some of the activities you used to enjoy.

What were some of the things that you did for fun last year that you no longer "have time for" or "just can't seem to get to"? Rate each activity for pleasure on the 0 to 10 scale.

Now, try the same exercise with activities from 3 years ago.

Finally, list some things you did for fun 5 years ago that you no longer do. Rate these activities for pleasure as well.

Are there any realistic reasons for no longer engaging in these activities? For example, if you once lived near the ocean and went sailing regularly but now live in a landlocked area, it may be difficult to go sailing routinely. However, you may find that you have nearly as much fun sailing on an inland lake. Sometimes activities you once engaged in are now difficult to be involved in for reasons beyond your control. However, with some effort, creative solutions can be found for seemingly impossible situations. The point is that, without examining those situations, you are more likely to stay in your unexamined routine.

Risk Taking

Another antidepressive activity involves risk taking. Often as we get older, we stop taking risks. We are not suggesting that you take up sky diving, but we are suggesting that you try some new things. Sometimes we become comfortable in a daily routine. However, what was once comfortable (like old clothes) may no longer fit and instead is constricting or boring. So, if you always go to a certain Italian restaurant on Saturday night, maybe trying the new Greek restaurant would be enjoyable as a break in routine. By taking that risk, you might find that you really enjoy the new place. Remember to ask yourself, "What's the worst that can happen?" You may not like the food as much, or you may enjoy the meal as well as your company for the evening.

Graded Tasks

You may feel incapable of altering the way you react to people and situations; you may also feel powerless to change the situations you face. If you see possible goals as too large or too far away, the technique of graded tasks breaks big jobs into smaller ones. Graded task assignments are derived from behavioral shaping strategies. Each small, sequential step approximates the eventual goal and helps you begin to expand activities in a gradual manner. It is important to take smaller steps at first to avoid failure and discouragement. Several smaller steps are far more effective than fewer larger steps. Ideally, the small steps can be rewarding as you start to take more of them. However, some individuals who have strong perfectionist tendencies may tell themselves that small steps are no big deal or not enough. If you are this type of individual, it is important to confront perfectionism with the thought that a journey of 1,000 miles starts with a single step and continues one step at a time. You have to start from where you are.

Clearly, the initial step in the sequence must be well within what you can do easily, and it must have some meaning for you. For example, for a severely depressed person, getting up and taking a walk or getting dressed in street clothes may be a monumental first step. Remember to acknowledge yourself for taking first steps; they are important in taking action and overcoming inertia.

Behavioral Rehearsal

Role playing is a very useful means of behavioral rehearsal. This technique is especially helpful when you can work on skill building with your therapist. The technique can be used to practice potential behaviors or interactions, such as dealing directly with a spouse, a significant other, a boss, or a friend. Your therapist can give you feedback about your performance and may even coach you on more effective responses and response styles. This strategy may be used for both skill building and practice of existing skills.

Social Skills Training

When we find ourselves having social problems, sometimes it happens because we are depressed. The important question—and it is a hard one—is this: "Did you have social difficulties before you were depressed?" If the answer is yes, then social skills training may be an essential part of your therapy. The problem may include lack of social skills and not just lack of motivation. Part of the work of your therapy may be helping you refine your social skills. Identification of specific skill problems and appropriate social skills training is customarily done in consultation with your therapist and practiced between sessions.

Relaxation Breathing Exercises

Anxiety frequently accompanies depression. Progressive relaxation, focused breathing, and meditation can relieve anxiety and help you gain a sense of control over your life. Progressive relaxation involves learning to relax small muscle groups, one at a time. It is a technique that you can learn with your therapist and begin practicing at home.

Another useful technique is patterned breathing, which involves learning to breathe according to a model, such as a square or rectangle, or according to a slower rhythm. You can learn to imagine a figure and breathe in through your nose to a count of 2 or 3 (whichever is more comfortable). Then hold your breath for a similar count. This is followed by relaxed exhalation through your mouth to a 3 or 4 count, followed again by holding your breath for a count of 2 or 3. This pattern is repeated 10 times. This slowed rhythm serves to stop hyperventilation. Imagining the figure is optional in helping you learn to breathe in a slower rhythm.

Chapter 5 Review

1. True or false: When you feel depressed, the best thing to do is to get into bed and wait until you feel better.

2. What do we mean by doing something to a point of *mastery?*

3. What do we mean by scheduling *pleasure?*

4. Which maintains the BEAST of depression, activity or procrastination?

5. How does a "graded task" work? What is an example of one you might try?

Life Situations and Vulnerability: The S of the BEAST

The goals of this chapter are

- to understand the relationship between mood and life circumstances
- to gain control when presented with life situations such as the following:
  - "I lost my job."
  - "My mother died."
  - "I am always in pain."
  - "I am getting old."
  - "My wife left me."
- to understand the role of vulnerability factors in depression
- to learn how to decrease vulnerability to depression by evaluating and prioritizing stressors

Understanding Life Events

You are often affected by events over which you have very little control. Wars start and end. The stock market goes up and down. Loved ones die. You become ill. You inherit money or incur debt. You are hired or fired. You fall in or out of love. The situations in your life are often linked to beliefs that affect your emotional equilibrium.

Beliefs prepare you for some situations and not for others. For example, believing there is danger everywhere may be lifesaving if you are on guard in a war zone. However, this same belief may be unduly stressful in other circumstances. If you believe that nothing good will ever happen, you may occasionally avoid disappointment, but you may also miss out on valuable experiences. These beliefs are often associated with depressed mood and an inability to recognize when good things do happen.

Even if you live in a safe environment, such beliefs may occur automatically regardless of their appropriateness to the situation. This automatic but inappropriate reaction may create unwarranted discomfort. In this chapter, you will find ways to identify situations accurately and change your thoughts about situations that may be getting in the way of your happiness and fulfillment. You will not be able to make all negative things go away, but you can get through difficult times by adjusting your thoughts.

The Unspoken Part of Life Situations

Life is full of surprises, problems, rewards, and crises. Good things are the source of joy and happiness. Stressors are the source of anxiety and depression. People are typically not happy or joyful when life has delivered a problem or crisis. However, if you look at an experience, you can see that not only the external circumstance, but also your internal perception of the circumstance contributes to depression. For example, consider the statements at the beginning of the chapter. Although each represents a huge life stressor, the unspoken assumptions make things worse. Look over each of the same statements again, with the implied but unspoken assumptions. See how much worse the unspoken assumption makes an already bad situation.

- "I lost my job (I will never find another)."
- "My mother died (I am all alone)."
- "I am always in pain (I cannot stand it)."
- "I am getting old (I will die soon)."
- "My wife left me (I cannot live without her)."

To illustrate this point further, if the person to whom these events occurred had a different view of the situation, the cognitive and emotional results would be quite different. Read the same statements with different assumptions.

- "I lost my job (Now I can get a job I really enjoy)."
- "My mother died (She is finally at rest after her long and painful illness)."
- "I am always in pain (I can still walk, which is better than being confined to a bed)."
- "I am getting old (I now have the opportunity to do things I never could before)."
- "My wife left me (I have learned from this experience and will seek a more compatible partner)."

Certain life events are indisputably negative. The good news is that they are usually time-limited and specific to certain situations. You can pull from other areas of your life, including therapy, to learn to view these situations in different ways. It is possible to derive (or create) meaning from such experiences, no matter how awful they seem. When you are feeling down, you may think that the weight of the world is on your shoulders. Your first goal should be to identify the things you *have* to deal with. For example, you may think you have a million things to deal with. On further examination, you find that really only five or six things require your immediate attention. Recognizing that even *one* stressor can be more than enough to overwhelm you, we are going to try to make each stressful situation more manageable and less damaging.

Identifying Stressors

The first step is to identify your stressors. Divide them into two groups. First, list the *specific* stressors. These stressors are easily identified and recognized, such as job loss. They are the clearly seen events and circumstances that may get you down. List the situations that are currently contributing to your depression.

Specific Stressors

1.

2.

3.

4.

5.

Now, identify the *nonspecific* stressors. This sort of stress is usually precipitated by a series of traumatic events, each in itself rather small. In combination they add up to a stressor that contributes to depression. An example is a traffic jam that makes you late for a meeting at your child's school. Identify a series of stressors that are more general in nature.

________________ + ________________ +

________________ + ________________ +

________________ + ________________ =

____

Vulnerability Factors

Vulnerability factors make you more likely to be affected by life situations, more sensitive to even small situational changes, and more reactive. They may cause you to overlook options for coping effectively and contribute to your failure to seek or initiate ways for coping. Review the following vulnerability factors, and indicate the ones that may apply to you. Specify a particular situation that might be affected.

1. Acute illness: When you are ill, your ability to cope with life stress decreases. Illness may range from a severe, debilitating sickness to more transient health problems such as headaches and viral infections. It is essential to be in consultation with a primary care physician so that these illnesses can be dealt with medically. Not seeing a medical doctor may increase the severity of depression.

   True Untrue

   How this affects me:

2. Chronic illness: In addition to acute illness, situations in which the health problem is chronic can lead to increased severity of suicidal thinking.

   True Untrue

   How this affects me:

3. Deterioration of health: In aging, there may be a loss of activity because the body cannot perform up to the expectations that were appropriate at other times in your life.

   True Untrue

   How this affects me:

4. Hunger: During times of food deprivation, you are more vulnerable to a variety of stimuli. Studies have indicated that people who are hungry should not shop for food because of the probability of overpurchasing.

   True Untrue

   How this affects me:

5. Anger: When you are angry, you may experience a loss of problem-solving ability. There may be a loss of impulse control or an increased response to stimuli that may usually be ignored.

   True Untrue

   How this affects me:

6. Fatigue: In a similar fashion, fatigue decreases both problem-solving strategies and impulse control.

   True Untrue

   How this affects me:

7. Loneliness: When you feel lonely, you may think that no one else understands you. You may be more sensitive about the interactions you have with other people.

   True Untrue

   How this affects me:

8. Major life loss: The loss of a significant other through death or divorce may lead you to think you have reduced options or that you do not care what happens to you.

   True Untrue

   How this affects me:

9. Poor problem-solving ability: Certain individuals may have impaired problem-solving ability. This deficit may not be obvious until the individual is placed in situations of great stress. Being able to deal with minor problems may never test the individual's ability.

   True Untrue

   How this affects me:

10. Substance abuse: Substance abuse can increase depression and suicidal thinking. Overall, substances tend to lower thresholds. Problems from this source may be of two types: acute problems with compromised judgment during periods of intoxication and more chronic problems with judgment that is impaired more generally.

    True Untrue

    How this affects me:

11. Chronic pain: Chronic pain almost always lowers thresholds. Its effects may range from discomfort and a negative view of the future to hopelessness.

    True Untrue

    How this affects me:

12. Poor impulse control: Some people have poor impulse control because of organic (hyperactivity) or functional problems. People with poor impulse control tend to act before they think things out.

    True Untrue

    How this affects me:

13. New life circumstance: Changing jobs, getting married, moving to a new house, having a child, and going away to school are all stressors that serve to lower thresholds and increase vulnerability.

    True Untrue

    How this affects me:

Evaluating Situation-Specific Vulnerability

Each of the vulnerability factors can lower your threshold for stress and expose you to stimuli that contribute to depression. Often, vulnerability factors are situation-specific and affect you most in certain areas of your life. Following is a list of life areas that are problematic for some individuals. What is your threshold to these life events? Using a scale from 1 to 100, evaluate how much stress or difficulty you can manage in each of the areas. For example, if it takes very little to get you down, you have a low threshold (1). If you are able to take an enormous amount of stress in a particular area without reacting with depression, you have a high threshold (100). On the following scales, indicate your threshold for stress by marking a "T" on the line. We have left spaces for you to write in other life stressors.

Low Vulnerability Threshold High Vulnerability Threshold

1. Dealing with parents

1——————————50——————————100

2. Dealing with work issues

1——————————50——————————100

3. Relationships

1——————————50——————————100

4. Sex

1——————————50——————————100

5. Dealing with children

1——————————50——————————100

6. Dealing with physical illness

1——————————50——————————100

7. Loss

1——————————50——————————100

8. Pressure to perform

1——————————50——————————100

9. Dealing with friends

1——————————50——————————100

10. Coping with social situations

1——————————50——————————100

11. Dealing with financial matters

1——————————50——————————100

12.

1——————————50——————————100

13.

1——————————50——————————100

14.

1——————————50——————————100

15.

1——————————50——————————100

By completing this exercise, you have probably discovered that your thresholds differ with different life events. If the stress in one area of your life is 50 and your threshold is 40, you will probably feel overwhelmed in that area. If the stress in one area is 80 and your threshold is 85 in that area, you are likely to be able to continue coping well. When the stress in one or more areas increases over the threshold, more than one stressor occurs, *or* the stressors reduce the overall threshold, you may respond with depression. Look over the areas on the list and determine if the actual amount of stress you are currently experiencing in each area is under or over your threshold. Indicate the amount of stress by placing an "S" on each line.

Coping with Difficult Life Situations

For those situations in which the amount of stress (S) currently exceeds your threshold (T), answer the following questions.

	Yes	No
Can someone else handle this for you?	○	○
Can you postpone the situation?	○	○
Have you dealt with situations like this before?	○	○
Do you know anyone who has dealt with this situation before?	○	○
Can you change parts of the situation?	○	○
Is the situation going to change with time?	○	○

Count the yes and no answers.

Totals ______ ______

If the number of no responses exceeds the yes responses, there is a greater chance for hopelessness and depression. Now answer the next set of questions. You will see that there are some very small changes to the questions.

	Yes	No
■ Is it possible that you do not have to deal with all of the situation by yourself?	○	○
■ Is it possible to postpone a small part of the situation?	○	○
■ Have you ever dealt with slightly similar situations?	○	○
■ Do you know anyone who has ever had to deal with anything like this before?	○	○
■ Is it possible that parts of the situation are more easily changeable?	○	○
■ Is it possible that the situation is going to change with time?	○	○

Count the yes and no answers.

Totals	______	______

Is there any difference in the number of yes responses between the first and second set of questions? You will probably have more yes answers the second time. The difference between the first set of questions and the second set is that in the first set there was little chance of change and more "all-or-nothing thinking." In the second set, we introduced the *possibility* of change and less all-or-nothing thinking.

Where do you go from here? The exercise you just completed illustrates the point that, by widening the scope of possibilities in coping with external stressors, hope is inspired. If you want to reach a goal, you need to do it one step at a time. By taking small steps, you can overcome large obstacles.

Look at the specific situations in which the stressors overreach your threshold and contribute to your depression. Choose one and ask yourself the second set of questions about it. Write down one small part of that situation with which you can start coping. After that, choose another small part and then another and another. You can use the coping with stressors worksheet for this exercise. (See Figure 6.1)

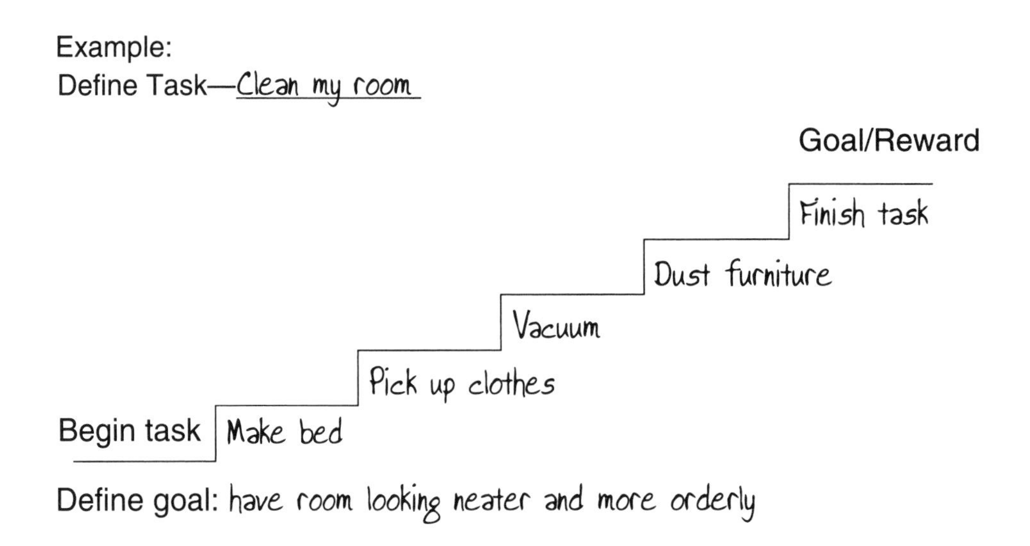

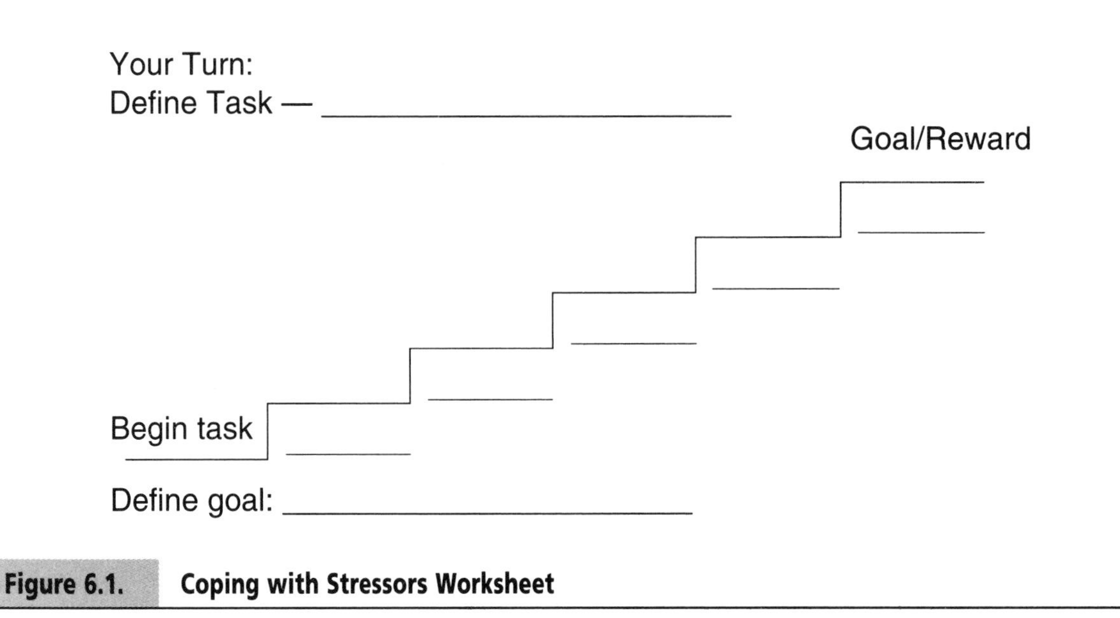

Figure 6.1. **Coping with Stressors Worksheet**

Prioritizing Stressors

A final strategy for combating stressors when you are feeling overwhelmed is to arrange them according to which problems need your attention first. This strategy breaks a seemingly overwhelming situation into smaller, more manageable parts. For example, Judy came to therapy for her depression. The number of things in her life that had gone wrong and were likely to go wrong overwhelmed her. She had just lost her job, was living on a small amount of savings, had not yet started collecting unemployment compensation, and had many unpaid bills.

During her therapy session she made a list of all of the things she thought needed her immediate attention. Her therapist asked her to separate the list into three separate lists. List number 1 contained things that could be put off for at least a day. List number 2 included things she could ask others to do or help with. Things on the third list needed attention that very day. When Judy was able to separate these stressors, she discovered that the list requiring immediate attention was much smaller than she had previously thought. She even found that some of those situations could be dealt with quite easily. In fact, one situation was to make a call to the telephone company, which was threatening to turn off her phone. Clearly, she could not postpone it. After role playing several different scenarios with her therapist, Judy made the call from her therapist's office. She found that her fear of being insulted, yelled at, or punished was not upheld. After Judy explained the situation, the customer relations representative suggested several solutions, including an extra week to pay a certain portion of the bill.

Chapter 6 Review

1. List the three major vulnerability factors that are likely to add to your depression.

2. What three life situations cause you the most discomfort or depression?

3. What effect do your identified life situations have on your mood?

4. Do negative life situations always have to lead to negative moods? How might you avoid this reaction?

Thoughts and Depression: The T of the BEAST

The goals of this chapter are

- to understand how your thoughts are categorized in the cognitive triad model
- to identify thinking patterns that maintain depression
- to understand the elements of cognitive distortions
- to develop ability to work with techniques for challenging cognitive bias
- to learn how to rework your thoughts and improve your mood with the Thought Record

In Chapter 2 we introduced the cognitive triad. The cognitive triad can help you start to divide the global experience of depression into smaller, more manageable pieces. The term *triad* describes the three negative views that characterize depression. Each view is characterized by thoughts that reflect that view. The first is the negative view you might have about yourself. These are the thoughts that include the personal pronouns *I, me,* or *my.* You might say to yourself:

- I am no good.
- Nobody likes me.
- My work is terrible.

The second element is the negative view and related thoughts that you might have about the world or your experience in the world. You might say to yourself:

- Life is unfair.
- People should be nicer.
- The world is an awful place.

Finally, there is the negative view and related thoughts you might have about your future. You might say to yourself:

- Things will never get any better.
- I will always suffer.
- There is no hope.

Many of life's problems can be categorized into at least one of these categories of negative views and related thoughts. The accumulated content in each of these three views is evident in how you see the world overall. Your feelings and behavior typically correspond with the negative content of these views. For example, if you view yourself as physically unattractive, you may then avoid situations in which physical attractiveness might be seen as a prerequisite for success (e.g., dating).

Negative View of Self

Write down the thoughts you have about yourself that are negative. For example, do you say to yourself, "I am stupid" or some other negative self-statements? Such negative statements are global and seem to come automatically. Do not stop now to evaluate whether these statements are true. What we would like you to do here is start to look at the negative things you say to and about yourself.

Negative View of the World

Now, write down the negative thoughts that you have about the world and your experiences. What ideas do you carry with you about *your* world? Do you say, "All men [or women] are jerks"? As before, do not stop yet to analyze whether these statements are true.

Negative View of the Future

How do you see the future—the rest of your life? Do you focus on the idea that "things will always be this bad"? Do you predict negative results for things you might try to do in the future? Write down any specific negative thoughts that you have about the future in the space below.

Now, review the groups of statements that you wrote to determine the degree to which your thoughts fit the cognitive triad model of depression. It is important for you to structure the program for relieving your depression first by paying special attention to the areas in which your thoughts are most negative. Personal issues relating to self, world, and future are different for each of us. Each part of the triad does not necessarily contribute equally to your experience of depression. By assessing the relative contribution of each of the three, you can begin to develop a clear understanding of your unique combination of negative thoughts. By including an assessment of each group of negative thoughts, your personalized program can be directed toward your own specific area of concern rather than toward vague, global problems.

Cognitive Distortions

As discussed in Chapter 2, distortions represent biased views that are not usually validated by other people. They represent a selectively narrow part of experience; usually negative. Distortions in thinking are frequently the initial focus of therapy because they are often easily identified. It is important for you to discover the distortions in your thinking by tracking your "automatic thoughts"—these spontaneous thoughts associated with certain moods and/or situations. These spontaneously generated thoughts can then be evaluated for the impact they have on your life. Recognizing these distortions and biases can point to underlying patterns in your thinking. The main purpose of discovering distortions is to allow you to begin to alter dysfunctional thoughts and thought patterns. Remember that people are usually biased because subjective personal experience influences perceptions. These biases become problematic when they are too extreme or are inappropriately relied upon. The following are examples of types of distorted thinking:

1. All-or-nothing thinking: thinking globally, considering only extreme options, although much of reality exists on a continuum. This is black or white with no shades of gray.

    I am either a success or a failure.

    Things are either completely right or absolutely wrong.

    I love you or I hate you.

2. Mind reading: thinking you know what others are thinking.

    They probably think I am incompetent.

    I just know that she disapproves.

    Even though people do not say so, I ***know*** how they *really* feel.

3. Emotional reasoning: the belief that if you feel something, it must be true and should be acted upon.

    I feel so inadequate, I must be inadequate.

    I feel so angry, I must express it.

    If I feel anxious, I should not go out.

4. Personalization: the belief that you are the target of difficulty.

    That comment was not just random; it must have been directed at me.

    Problems always emerge when I am in a hurry.

    Someone is always picking on me.

5. Overgeneralization: assuming that one incident applies to all others.

    Everything I do turns out wrong.

    It does not matter what my choices are; they always fall flat.

    My boyfriend broke up with me; no one wants me.

6. Catastrophizing: assuming the worst.

    If I go to the party, there will be terrible consequences.

    I better not try because I might fail, and I could not stand that.

    My fiancée broke our engagement; I will never get married.

7. Should and shouldn't statements: reflecting a judgmental attitude.

    I should visit my family every time they want me to.

    They should be nicer to me.

    I should not feel angry [or scared or anxious].

8. Need for control: the belief that absolute control is necessary.

    If I am not in complete control all the time, I am in danger of going out of control.

    I must be able to control everything in my life.

    I cannot let anyone else help me with this task. They might do it wrong.

9. Negative comparisons: viewing your performance in comparison to others.

    I am not as competent as my co-workers or supervisors.

    Compared with others, there is clearly something flawed about me.

    Even though it is OK for other people to make mistakes, it is not OK for me to.

10. Disqualifying the positive: difficulty believing positive experience.

    This success experience was only a fluke.

    That compliment was unwarranted.

    Even though she said she liked my work, I know she did not mean it.

11. Perfectionism: the need to be perfect.

    If I cannot do everything perfectly, I will be criticized and feel like a failure.

    Doing merely an adequate job is akin to being a failure.

    When I make a mistake, I feel worthless.

12. Selective abstraction: missing the big picture.

    All those compliments do not matter. This criticism is the only thing that matters.

    I seem to dwell on the negative details and don't pay attention to the positive aspects of a situation.

    Even though I received an overall positive review, I think that I am not doing a good job.

13. Externalization of self-worth: looking to others for self-validation.

    My worth is dependent upon what others think of me.

    They think I am ____________________ (e.g., stupid, lazy); they must be right.

    I am not OK unless I am pleasing others.

14. If-only thinking: wishful or regretful thinking.

    If only my situation were different, all of my problems would. . . .

    If only I were taller, she would like me.

    If only I had not ____________________________________ (e.g., made that decision, done that), I would be happy now.

15. Worry helps: believing that worrying equates with protection.

    If I think about it long enough, it will be resolved.

    One cannot be too concerned.

    If I forget to worry or let down my guard, something bad might happen.

16. If I ignore it: avoidance as a defense.

    If I ignore it, maybe it will go away.

    If I do not pay attention, I will not be held responsible.

    What I don't know won't hurt me.

17. Fairness: the belief that life should always work out the way you think it should.

    Life should be fair.

    People should be fair.

    Good behavior should always be rewarded.

18. I must be right: rigidly maintaining that one is right in all circumstances, despite contrary evidence.

    I must prove that I am right; being wrong is unacceptable.

    To be wrong is to be unforgivable or a bad person.

    If I am wrong about one thing, it means I am wrong about everything.

19. I can't stand it: the belief that a specific situation or feeling is intolerable.

    I cannot stand to be angry without exploding.

    I cannot stand not knowing if he or she loves me; I must ask.

    If I experience happiness, something horrible will happen.

20. I can't live without. . . .: the belief that life is not worth living if a desire is unattainable.

    I cannot live without a man/woman.

    If I were in a relationship, all my problems would be solved.

    I cannot survive if I am alone.

Review the list of distortions above, and circle those you are most likely to use. Write the ones you use most frequently in the following space. You may need to come back to this section later to add distortions because these thoughts may occur automatically and be embedded in other thinking to the extent that they are difficult to recognize.

1.

2.

3.

4.

5.

6.

Changing Your Cognitive Patterns: Some Techniques

Cognitive techniques are useful in challenging distorted and negative thinking patterns. Therapists use these techniques to examine and question such patterns. This therapeutic dialogue is an important part of cognitive therapy. This section lists such techniques and explains their purposes. You are encouraged to discuss these methods with your therapist. The Appendix at the end of this workbook illustrates each technique with sample dialogues that might occur in a therapy session. We have used the term "Depressed you" to indicate that when you are depressed you use many more negative thoughts to describe yourself. The "Challenger" is your internal questioner who is going to find out what these thoughts are really about. The Challenger will function much like your therapist to widen your perspective and allow you to respond to the evidence you may not be attending to. You are encouraged to review the examples in the Appendix and apply them to your own internal dialogue.

Cognitive Therapy Techniques

1. Questioning what you really mean
2. Questioning the evidence
3. Reattribution
4. Examining options and alternatives
5. Decatastrophizing
6. Examining expected consequences
7. Listing advantages and disadvantages
8. Turning adversity to advantage
9. Labeling distortions
10. Guided association and discovery
11. Using paradox or exaggeration
12. Scaling
13. Replacement imagery
14. Cognitive rehearsal
15. Self-instruction or coaching
16. Thought stopping
17. Focusing

1. Questioning What You Really Mean

You may not completely understand the terms you are using. If a group of 100 people were asked to describe *depression,* you would probably hear 100 different definitions. Descriptions might include words like *sadness, the blues, hopelessness, sleep difficulties, sluggishness, slowed thinking, pessimism, apathy,* and *eating problems.* Given the varying meanings that words have, *it is essential to question what you mean when you use certain words.* (See Example 1 in the Appendix.)

Exercise: List some of the negative words you use to describe yourself. Then go back and challenge each word to determine what it really means to you.

Word I Use to Describe Myself	Challenge the Word	What Do I Really Mean?
Example: Loser	?	I make many mistakes.
________________	?	________________
________________	?	________________
________________	?	________________
________________	?	________________
________________	?	________________
________________	?	________________
________________	?	________________
________________	?	________________
________________	?	________________
________________	?	________________
________________	?	________________
________________	?	________________
________________	?	________________
________________	?	________________
________________	?	________________
________________	?	________________

In instances where the meaning of these words is negative, go back and ask yourself if there is evidence to support your self-defeating opinion. You will learn more about this technique in the next exercise.

2. Questioning the Evidence

One effective way to challenge a dysfunctional thought is to examine the extent to which the thought is supported by available evidence. Ask yourself if other interpretations are more reasonable. It is essential to teach the "Depressed you" to question the evidence that you are using to maintain and strengthen an idea or belief. When you use selective abstraction, you may ignore major pieces of data and focus on the few aspects that support your depressive views. By questioning the evidence, you broaden your focus to include the entire reality rather than just the narrowly focused negative view. Even the slightest doubt in your initial, fixed belief could be the first step toward meaningful progress. (See Example 2 in the Appendix.)

Exercise: Select three negative assumptions you have about yourself and your life. List them here. Then go back and challenge the evidence for each assumption.

	Negative Assumption	Evidence
1.	______________________	______________________
	______________________	______________________
	______________________	______________________
2.	______________________	______________________
	______________________	______________________
	______________________	______________________
3.	______________________	______________________
	______________________	______________________
	______________________	______________________

3. Reattribution

A common statement from individuals who are depressed is "It's all my fault," especially in situations of relationship difficulty. Some individuals take total responsibility for situations; others tend to blame someone else and take no responsibility whatsoever. By becoming a "Challenger," you can help yourself begin to distribute responsibility in a more realistic and accurate manner. By taking the middle ground, you can help the depressed you reattribute responsibility and not take all the blame or unrealistically shift all the blame to someone else. (See Example 3 in the Appendix.)

Exercise: List negative events or circumstances for which you feel totally at fault. Then go back and ask yourself if anyone, other than yourself, may have shared in the responsibility.

Negative Event That's "All My Fault"	Anyone Else Who May Be Involved
1.	
2.	
3.	

The purpose of this exercise is not to shift blame entirely from you to someone else but rather to reveal the fact that many circumstances are associated with a combination of people and events.

4. Examining Options and Alternatives

People who are suicidal see themselves as having lost all hope. Death might be the easiest choice. Thoughts of suicide represent an inability to think of other alternatives. The goal of this technique is to counter the inertia of depression by generating other options. Even one additional choice challenges the cognitive distortion that there are no alternatives. (See Example 4 in the Appendix.)

Exercise: Make a list of situations in which you believe you had no options. Then list one or more alternatives that have become clear as you look back on the situation. If you have difficulty with this, consult with your therapist or someone whose judgment you respect.

Situation in Which I Had "No Options"	Looking Back Now, I See These Other Options
1.	
2.	

3. ______________________ ______________________

______________________ ______________________

______________________ ______________________

5. Decatastrophizing

When you catastrophize, you imagine the worst thing that could happen and then believe it will. Another way people catastrophize is to engage in "what if" thinking, imagining all the things that could go wrong. If you see an experience as potentially catastrophic, you can work to challenge whether you are overestimating the potential effects of the situation. Questions you might ask include: What is the worst thing that can happen? Could I survive that? If it does happen, how will my life be different 3 months from now? (See Example 5 in the Appendix.)

Exercise: First, write down an event or circumstance that you believed would lead to a catastrophe or disaster. Next, write what you thought would happen and then what actually happened.

Event/Circumstance	Expected Catastrophe	What Actually Happened
1. ______________	______________	______________
______________	______________	______________
______________	______________	______________
2. ______________	______________	______________
______________	______________	______________
______________	______________	______________
3. ______________	______________	______________
______________	______________	______________
______________	______________	______________

This exercise is intended to remind you that consequences in the past have not always matched your catastrophic thinking. Even though bad things happened, the world did not end.

6. Examining Expected Consequences

In this technique, you are asked to think about a situation and describe your concerns and expectations related to it. Often, describing expectations can reveal misperceptions and irrational thinking. Alternatively, if the anticipated consequences are likely, you can realistically assess danger and develop effective coping strategies. An active examination of the style, format, and content of your expectations can yield good material for working with your therapist and challenging irrational thinking. (See Example 6 in the Appendix.)

Exercise: List any negative expectations of people or events that may frighten you or negatively influence your behavior. Rank the chances that such an event will happen on a scale from 0–100%, and then list one to three options that may be appropriate to that expectation. You may want to rank-order these options in terms of effectiveness.

	Negative Expectation	Chance of This Happening (0–100%)	If This Did Happen, I Would
1.	________________	________________	________________
	________________	________________	________________
	________________	________________	________________
2.	________________	________________	________________
	________________	________________	________________
	________________	________________	________________
3.	________________	________________	________________
	________________	________________	________________
	________________	________________	________________

7. Listing Advantages and Disadvantages

Another approach is to look at the pros and cons of the beliefs that maintain depression. By focusing on the advantages and disadvantages of a particular behavior or way of thinking, you can achieve a more reasonable and adaptive perspective. This technique can be used to examine the adaptiveness of acting, thinking, and feeling certain ways. Although individuals who are depressed often claim that they cannot control their feelings, viewing personal options from a broader perspective can enhance your view of choices and your personal control. (See Example 7 in the Appendix.)

Exercise: List situations that are troublesome for you. Then, evaluate your different options for resolving each situation by listing advantages and disadvantages.

Specific Situation:

Options for Resolving Situation	Advantages	Disadvantages
1. ____________________	____________________	____________________
____________________	____________________	____________________
____________________	____________________	____________________
2. ____________________	____________________	____________________
____________________	____________________	____________________
____________________	____________________	____________________
3. ____________________	____________________	____________________
____________________	____________________	____________________
____________________	____________________	____________________

Specific Situation:

Options for Resolving Situation	Advantages	Disadvantages
1. ____________________	____________________	____________________
____________________	____________________	____________________
____________________	____________________	____________________

2. ____________ ____________ ____________

____________ ____________ ____________

____________ ____________ ____________

3. ____________ ____________ ____________

____________ ____________ ____________

____________ ____________ ____________

8. Turning Adversity to Advantage

As is often the case, for each thing lost, something important is gained. Sometimes what seems like a disaster can be used to your advantage. Losing your job can be a disaster but may be the entry point to a better job or even a new career. A deadline may seem oppressive and unfair but may be used as a motivator. This technique asks the depressed you to look for potential creative or adaptive outcomes. Looking for the positives of a difficult situation can be challenging. The depressed you will sometimes respond with even greater negativity when the challenger points out positive possibilities. You may accuse the challenger of being unrealistic. The challenger can point out that the positive view is no less real than the negative view. (See Example 8 in the Appendix.)

Exercise: Think of negative events that have happened to you. For each event, try to think of one positive outcome or one thing that you learned from the event.

Negative Event	Positive Outcome (creative or adaptive)
1. ____________	1. ____________
2. ____________	2. ____________
3. ____________	3. ____________
4. ____________	4. ____________

9. Labeling Distortions

One of the first steps toward self-knowledge is identification of your own distortions or errors of thinking. Many individuals who are depressed may find it useful to label the cognitive distortions they notice among their automatic thoughts. Although not essential for improvement, labeling is often helpful because it helps you see things from a cognitive therapy perspective, and you understand the style and format of your distortions. *Feeling Good* (Burns, 1980) is an excellent self-help book for learning more about cognitive distortions. (See Example 9 in the Appendix.)

Exercise: Review the list of cognitive distortions mentioned previously. Practice labeling your negative thoughts using the distortions provided.

	Thought	Type of Distortion
1.	____________________	____________________
	____________________	____________________
	____________________	____________________
2.	____________________	____________________
	____________________	____________________
	____________________	____________________
3.	____________________	____________________
	____________________	____________________
	____________________	____________________

10. Guided Association and Discovery

Through simple questions like "Then what?" and "What would that mean?" the challenger can help the depressed you explore the significance you see in events and potentially uncover underlying assumptions and beliefs you were not previously aware of. Using the chained or guided association technique, the challenger works with the depressed you to connect ideas, thoughts, and images. Asking questions like "What evidence do we have that that is true?" allows the challenger to guide the depressed you toward your therapeutic goals. The guided association can be employed in helping the depressed you identify underlying assumptions or beliefs. This process is like peeling an onion, layer by layer. (See Example 10 in the Appendix.)

Exercise: Use guided association to challenge three negative thoughts.

	Negative Thought / Assumption	Challenger's Questions	Answers
1.	______________	______________	______________
	______________	______________	______________
	______________	______________	______________

2. ____________________ ____________________ ____________________

____________________ ____________________ ____________________

____________________ ____________________ ____________________

3. ____________________ ____________________ ____________________

____________________ ____________________ ____________________

____________________ ____________________ ____________________

11. Using Paradox or Exaggeration

Ironically, taking an idea to its extreme can make it possible to view a situation or thought from a more realistic position. (See Example 11 in the Appendix.)

Exercise: Search for a negative thought you might have that may be exaggerated or extreme. Question yourself on it. Try saying it in an even more exaggerated way (e.g., I am unattractive; I really look like the Wicked Witch of the West). Ask yourself if your negative thought is realistic.

Extreme negative thought:

Question: Is this thought realistic?

Answer: ____

____

____

Extreme negative thought:

Question: Is this thought realistic?

Answer: ____

____

____

12. Scaling

Scaling is particularly useful for individuals who tend to see things as all or nothing, black or white. The technique of scaling—viewing things as existing on a continuum—helps people be more descriptive and therefore more objective. (See Example 12 in the Appendix.)

Exercise: Rate events using this mood measure.

Event: ____

How sad were you?

1————————————50————————————100
Not sad Extremely sad

Event: ____

How angry were you?

1————————————50————————————100
Not angry Extremely angry

Event: ____

How anxious were you?

1————————————50————————————100
Not anxious Extremely anxious

13. Replacement Imagery

Not all automatic thoughts are verbal. Images and dreams can be valuable sources of material in therapy. If you have dysfunctional images, you can generate more effective coping images to replace the depressing or anxiety-producing ones. Athletes have discovered that imagining specific successful performances can lead to increased actual performance during competition.

Similarly, the content of dreams can be examined from a cognitive perspective. Cognitive therapists view dreams as the active expression of the person.

The following example demonstrates replacement imagery. A 31-year-old woman reported the following dream: "I was sitting on the couch when out from the opposite wall came this huge snake. It struck at me with incredible speed, giving me no time to move away. It sank its fangs into my arm. All I could do was look at it and comment on the pain and the fact that it was biting me. I woke up feeling anxious and frightened."

The basic cognitive elements were her view of herself as helpless and her perceived inability to effectively react. These cognitive positions paralleled her dysfunctional cognitions in her waking state. She was extremely effective on her job but often felt anxious when called upon to be assertive. Her therapist might help her restructure the experience by asking what she might have done differently in the dream. She could restructure the scene as she wished, now in her attentive, reflective state. As a challenger, how might she encourage herself to use more adaptive skills?

At first, she restructured the dream tentatively, by visualizing herself trying to hold something over the snake hole in the wall. With further encouragement and some modeling from the therapist or the challenger, she restructured the scene so that she immediately severed the snake's head. As she restructured the dream to one in which she took greater control and asserted herself, there was an immediate affect shift from anxiety to relief.

In another technique, the dream is revisualized for the primary purpose of altering the negative elements. The snake could become a Sesame Street character, or the dreamer could offer the snake a treat or have a transparent shield. In restructuring the dream or image, a positive outcome can be effected. (See Example 13 in the Appendix.)

Exercise: Summarize one of your own dreams and then restructure it.

Original Dream:

Restructured Dream:

14. Cognitive Rehearsal

By visualizing an event in your mind, you can practice particular behaviors mentally. A number of athletes use this technique to enhance performance. By first generating a reasonable scene and practicing it mentally, you can investigate several possibilities by running each of them through your mind like a videotape. Pilots practice on a flight simulator to gain skills in this way. (See Example 14 in the Appendix.)

Exercise: Think of something you would like to learn how to do or do better.

Create a visual scenario with phases, and imagine specific steps that might lead to the desired result.

Scene 1:

Scene 2:

Scene 3:

Goal:

15. Self-Instruction or Coaching

The same process used in self-criticism can be used to learn and enhance new skills. For example, in learning impulse control, you can start with direct verbalization by saying self-instructions out loud. With practice, you learn to say the instructions without actual verbalizations, and eventually the instructions become more automatic. You can teach yourself to offer direct self-instructions or, in some cases, counterinstructions. In this technique, the challenger is not introducing anything new to the depressed you. Rather, you can utilize, change, and strengthen a technique that you have used before. (See Example 15 in the Appendix.)

Exercise: Think of a situation in which you wish you could curb your impulse to act until you have cooled down or thought the situation over.

What are some things you would like to tell yourself if you could wait before reacting to the situation?

16. Thought Stopping

Dysfunctional thoughts often have a snowball effect. What may start as an insignificant problem can gather weight and momentum. Once on a roll, the thoughts seem to have a force of their own and are very hard to stop. Thought stopping is best used when the thoughts first start, rather than in the middle of the process. The depressed you can be taught to picture a stop sign, hear a bell, picture a wall, or say the word *stop* out loud or clap your hands. This technique may be practiced in a session with your therapist. You can then remind yourself of your success at stopping or interfering with your thoughts in your session or when you are practicing on your own between sessions. (See Example 16 in the Appendix.)

Exercise: What are some repetitive negative thoughts that emerge for you that you would like to stop? List them and then practice stopping them by saying, "Stop!"

____ Stop!

____ Stop!

____ Stop!

____ Stop!

____ Stop!

____ Stop!

____ Stop!

____ Stop!

____ Stop!

____ Stop!

17. Focusing

There is a limit to how many things you can think about at once. By occupying your mind with neutral thoughts or one neutral word, you can block dysfunctional thoughts. You might repeat a neutral word or sound, count slowly, focus on calming and pleasant images, or concentrate on external stimuli. Although this technique is short-term in nature, it gives the depressed you time to establish some degree of control over your thinking. To practice this technique, set aside 10 to 15 minutes twice a day, sit comfortably, close your eyes, and relax. (See Example 17 in the Appendix.)

Exercise: For the negative thoughts you listed in the previous exercise, try focusing on something neutral or pleasant to interrupt the thoughts. Each time you become aware that you have drifted back to your negative thoughts, simply refocus back to your replacement thoughts or image. You will do this again and again.

____ Refocus

____ Refocus

____ Refocus

____ Refocus

____ Refocus

____ Refocus

____ Refocus

____ Refocus

____ Refocus

____ Refocus

The Automatic Thought Record

The Thought Record presented in this chapter (see Figures 7.1 and 7.2) is one of the most widely used methods in therapy for helping change thinking patterns and levels of emotional distress. It is well worth spending time on and practicing the use of this method. It is not learned immediately. Take time to collect information about distressing situations between sessions and write them down. You can apply your understanding of the cognitive distortions and the cognitive therapy techniques using this format in your responses to automatic thoughts. Following are some basic ground rules for transcribing your experience onto the Thought Record.

Situation

This is a neutral description of what you are experiencing as you find yourself feeling emotional distress. It is "just the facts" and not a time to editorialize. Describe what you are doing and/or where you are while you are feeling bad.

Emotions

These are the feeling(s) you are experiencing during the situation you described. A feeling is usually a word or two (i.e., anxious, sad, afraid, angry, etc.), not a description of how, what, or why. Your therapist can help you if you have difficulty identifying exactly what you feel. Often people confuse thoughts and feelings. The feeling is associated with the previous column (your situation) and the next column (your automatic thought). You should rate the intensity of your feelings on a scale of 1–100%, wth 1% representing no distress and 100% representing the most intense feelings you have ever felt.

Automatic Thoughts

This is the thought(s) that are going through your mind associated with the feeling(s) you reported in the previous column. You should also rate your belief in these thoughts on a scale of 1–100%, with 1% representing no belief and 100% representing a great amount of belief in these thoughts.

Adaptive Thoughts

These are your responses to the automatic thoughts. They involve the principles you have just read about in the section on cognitive therapy techniques. You should also rate your belief in these adaptive thoughts on a scale of 1–100%, with 1% representing no belief and 100% representing a great amount of belief. Following are some other rules of thumb when you use this method.

1. Address only one automatic thought at a time. If you have several automatic thoughts associated with the feeling, chose the one that seems the strongest. You can go back to the others later, if the distress you are feeling is still very strong.
2. Try to come up with at least three adaptive thought responses for each automatic thought. They should be specific and contain evidence (preferably from your life and experience) to dispute or offer alternatives to the content of the automatic thought. If the thought is a realistic problem, problem-solving skill building can be a part of the contents you write in this column.
3. Use descriptive rather than judgmental or value-laden language. Be compassionate to yourself about what you are feeling and move away from being self-punitive. Identify any language distortions, like "should," "have to," "must," "always," and "never."

Examples of Adaptive Thoughts

Last time I missed a deadline, no one was that upset because they knew I put in a good effort. (95%)

I want to avoid such dramatic language, he would not try to hurt me for a mistake, let alone kill me. (100%)

Wait a second, I have overlooked the 6-month severence pay that I can live on as I try to find another job. (100%)

I have good credentials and even though it will be difficult, I think I can find something else; if not, I can take some temp work until I do. (80%)

Outcome

Here you describe what happened as a result of your actions and re-rate your feelings and thoughts. You should also add any new feelings or thoughts you may have about what is affecting you.

It is recommended that you photocopy the blank Thought Record (see Figure 7.1) and use it when you have distressing feelings. (See Figure 7.2 for a completed example.)

Figure 7.3 presents a chart for you to list when you practiced the techniques listed in this chapter. You may want to photocopy it so you can record your practice over a period of weeks.

Date and Time	Situation (Describe the circumstances)	Emotions (Write your feelings and rate them on a 0–100% scale)	Automatic Thoughts (Write your automatic thoughts and rate your belief in them on a 0–100% scale)	Adaptive Thoughts (Write an adaptive thought and rate your belief in it on a 0–100% scale)	Outcome (Describe what happened as the result of your actions)

Figure 7.1. **Thought Record**

Date and Time	Situation (Describe the circumstances)	Emotions (Write your feelings and rate them on a 0–100% scale)	Automatic Thoughts (Write your automatic thoughts and rate your belief in them on a 0–100% scale)	Adaptive Thoughts (Write an adaptive thought and rate your belief in it on a 0–100% scale)	Outcome (Describe what happened as the result of your actions)
11-10-98 5:15 pm	I am in the car and thinking anout the things I forgot to do at work.	Anxious (90%) Fearful (95%)	If I don't get the work done for my boss, he's going to kill me! (95%)	I have a good record with my boss because I usually get the work done early. (90%)	Anxiety is reduced to 40%. Fear is at 50%. New feelings: Calm-60% Confident-55%
11-11-98 3:45 pm	I was told that the job ends in 30 days and I will be laid off.	Depressed (80%) Hopeless (90%)	I won't be able to support my family if I don't have this job. (99%)	I knew when I started here that this was not my life's work. (70%) We have saved money and my parents are able to help us. (70%)	Depression is reduced to 60% Hopelessness (40%)

Figure 7.2. **Example Thought Record**

Technique	Day 1	Day 2	Day 3	Day 4	Day 5	Day 6	Day 7
1							
2							
3							
4							
5							
6							
7							
8							
9							
10							
11							
12							
13							
14							
15							
16							
17							
Thought Record							

Figure 7.3. Cognitive Therapy Techniques Practice Chart

Chapter 7 Review

1. Name three cognitive distortions.

2. Why is it important to question yourself when you are depressed or anxious?

3. Name five techniques for improving your depression.

4. How can cognitive rehearsal help with a personal problem?

Final Words of Hope

Will Depression Come Back?

So now you are feeling somewhat better. You may ask yourself, "Will the depression come back?" Evidence suggests that the answer is "Perhaps." For some people who have a serious problem of low mood, a single episode is all they experience. Other people experience a recurrence of their low mood after a period of normal mood. The important point is that now you are better prepared because you have a number of ways to reduce the severity of depression and limit how long it lasts. Even if low mood returns, it can have less effect on your life.

Am I Finished?

A second question you may ask yourself is "Am I finished?" You may be saying, "Now that I am less depressed, I never have to work at dealing with my mood." That would be like saying, "Now that I have lost 5 pounds, I'm going to eat a gallon of ice cream." What is more likely is that you have recovered from a period of low mood and are getting back on track with your life. Just like any other skill, practicing what you have learned to monitor and confront low mood is important. The exercises that you have gone through in this program are not "used up." You should continue to use them to maximize the quality of your life, and they must be practiced periodically. You have to give yourself a maintenance contract for your life.

Using your emotion and mood skills regularly does not mean that you remain in "therapy" or "counseling" for the rest of your life, any more than learning how to play tennis means you work with a coach for the rest of your life. However, maintaining your realistic and positive mood is important. Many of the skills you have mastered are now incorporated into your everyday life. They can also help you in two very important ways in the days and weeks to come. You can use the skills you have mastered in this program to better monitor your day-to-day mood and the thoughts and circumstances that accompany them. This habit will help you identify potential problems early. Early identification of abnormally low mood can offer you the opportunity to help yourself in another important way. By rationally challenging your dysfunctional thoughts, you may catch low mood early and prevent it from worsening. Therefore, the combination of your early warning skills in discovering a potential problem and your self-help skills in directly confronting the issue of low mood can help you maintain the achievements of these past weeks.

Case Examples

Sara

Sara was a student who was depressed and had many negative thoughts about herself and the future. She habitually thought and acted in ways that maintained her depression, similar to those you have read about in this workbook. She participated in therapy, and her mood improved significantly in about 4 months. However, when she announced that she thought she had "conquered" her depression and that she was determined never to feel this way again, she needed a little more work to gain perspective on what she had accomplished.

Sara appeared to have inadvertently applied the distortion of all-or-nothing thinking to her improved condition. Odd as it may seem, distortions or biases in thinking apply to feeling good, too! This is why a transition process occurs in therapy when a therapist and client discuss what improvement was made with cognitive therapy, and what to expect in the future. Sara's therapist asked her about the flip side of low self-confidence, which is overconfidence. Too little or too much confidence seldom serves people well. The tendency to overstate can become an exaggeration of reality. When she reflected on what she had been through, Sara recognized that her depression was very powerful and not necessarily a condition she knew everything about. Her therapist agreed and confided that he, too, did not know all there was to know about this common emotional problem. Cognitive therapists are discovering new ways to help their clients all the time. It is important that neither therapists nor clients become too confident that they know everything about the complexities of mood and affect. We have developed significant methods to recover from depression. If you used this program well, you are better prepared for future depressive episodes but not invulnerable.

Your improvement means that your strength and defenses have gotten better through your effort. If you had decided to improve your physical condition by joining a fitness center, you might exercise several times a week, get a personal trainer, and focus on strengthening your weaknesses. Let's say you changed your appearance and became lean and limber. If you really like your accomplishments, you would be ill advised to stop all exercise and go back to your old routine. If a person wants to stay in shape physically and emotionally, it requires maintenance and effort. Many people experience some relapse in maintaining themselves in good shape either physically or mentally. If you are aware of this human tendency to fall back to old habits and routines, you are more likely to approach such problems pragmatically and without condemnation. Then, the possibilities of reapplying the techniques that work for improvement increase.

John

With therapy, John successfully improved his mood a couple of years ago. However, the depression came back. This time, he was so disgusted with himself that he was almost dragged into treatment by his brother. He told his therapist he was ashamed that he was back in the same poor shape that he was in so long ago. An area he had difficulty with in his first effort in therapy was self-compassion. He tended to be critical and perfectionistic, and when he was depressed, he judged himself harshly. It became easier for him to reapply methods of cognitive therapy once he acknowledged that he did not do well when criticized by others. Also, he had more difficulty dealing with problems when he was overcritical in his own self-talk. His second round of therapy was even more successful than the first. This is not an uncommon story.

One aspect of successfully managing depression is recognizing when our prevention and maintenance efforts are weakening. In such instances, it may be necessary to schedule a booster session with your therapist. Consultations such as these can reinforce skills previously learned in therapy as well as enhance them.

One Last Story About the Future

If you have dealt with some significant problems in your life while in therapy, you know these aren't the last problems you will have. You may have come to treatment as a result of losing a job or starting a new one. You may have had a love relationship end badly or perhaps in divorce. You could have made a mistake in judgment and have done things to disappoint others and yourself. There are no certificates, credentials, special knowledge, or passes that allow you to graduate into a stress-free existence without ever experiencing problems and disappointments again. Discouragement, success, and even boredom in the future are all possibilities in parts of your life. Sometimes fortune cookies, motivational speakers, and psychic friends provide the vague promises of solving almost all your problems now and forever. The authors have found that such promises are unrealistic and misleading. Probably the most reasonable assurance your therapist can provide is that you are better prepared to navigate through life so that you might appreciate the good events and deal adequately when things go wrong. Your therapy is skill-building in solving problems, accepting yourself, and finding compassion for others and for yourself. It takes practice and discipline. There is no pill, perfect shield or piece of advice that gives a human being an immunity from the difficulties of life. However, you may come to know more about the relativity of what can bring a sense of well-being. As Shakespeare wrote in *Hamlet*, "there is nothing either good or bad but thinking makes it so" (*Hamlet,* Act II, Scene II).

When It Comes Back

All moods are temporary. You now have more options on how to handle depression than you did before you started reading this workbook and trying the cognitive therapy methods. It is important to expect that some things will get you down. When they do, use these methods again. Your success with this program is not over just because you might be feeling better. It is because you understand the methods and can use them again and again. This is because life's ups and downs are practically a certainty. If you can improve your mood just a bit, you are making progress. If the problems continue, get a booster session or even a few additional sessions with a cognitive therapist in your area.

The following parable (1997 Pete Seeger, used with permission) may help us reflect on the pursuit of creating meaning in our lives (Seeger & Blood, 1997):

> **Once there was a king who had three sons, and he wanted to give them a good education. He called in his wise men. He said, "I want you to boil down all the world's wisdom into one book; I'll give it to my sons and have them memorize it." It took them a year; they came back with a volume bound in leather, trimmed in gold. The king leafed through it. "Hm, very good." He turns to his sons. "Learn it!" Now he turned to the wise men. He said, "You did such a good job with that, see if you can boil down all the world's wisdom into one sentence."**
>
> **It took them five years. They came back and bowed low. "Your majesty, the sentence is 'This too shall pass.'" The king didn't like that so well. He said, "See if you can boil down all the world's wisdom into one word." It took them ten years. When they came back, their beards were draping on the ground.**
>
> **They bowed low. "Your majesty! The word is, (pause) 'Maybe.'"**

Maybe cognitive therapy has helped you. There is a lot of reason to have confidence in the methods described in this workbook and in yourself. You don't know what good (or bad) events await you. With effort applied in meaningful ways, you can have a better life. This applies to anyone. These methods *do* work. The authors' colleagues all around the world have conducted scientific outcome studies that over and over again show how the ideas and methods described in this workbook are effective with improving affect and mood for people who suffer with depression. Cognitive therapy may be one of the most researched set of successful methods for getting people relief from depression that currently exists! It's up to you to make use of the techniques and ideas in this book. Are you wanting and willing to try? We hope so.

Examples of Cognitive Therapy Techniques

Example 1: Questioning What You Really Mean

Depressed you: I'm a loser!

Challenger: You call yourself a loser. Just what is a loser? What does being a loser mean to you?

Depressed you: You know, a *loser.* I can't do anything right. Nobody likes me.

Challenger: OK, that's a good start. It's important to know specifically what *you* mean when you use terms that don't have a clear meaning, like *loser.*

Example 2: Questioning the Evidence

Depressed you: There is no way in the world that he would be interested in me.

Challenger: Before you become depressed, how do you know that he's not interested?

Depressed you: Come on. If he were interested in me, he would have asked me out—and he hasn't.

Challenger: Let's look at all the evidence. That's true, he hasn't asked you out yet. Has he done anything else to let you know he's interested? Does he spend time talking to you? How about the small gifts he has bought for you?

Depressed you: That's all true, but the real test is whether he asks me out.

Challenger: So the evidence at this point is, at least, mixed?

Depressed you: Well, yes, I suppose.

Example 3: Reattribution

Depressed you: It's all my fault. I really screwed things up this time. If only I could have handled things differently, that contract would have come through. If only I hadn't been so demanding. I blew it.

Challenger: You said before that much of your work on this project was good, so it sounds as if there may have been some other factors that kept you from getting this contract. Is it really *all* your fault that things didn't work out?

Depressed you: Yes. Who else could it be?

Challenger: What about the delays your boss put on the project? What about the recent change in management in your company? I know that you feel that it was all your fault. I think it might be helpful, though, to examine all of the roles played in this project.

Depressed you: Well, we have been shorthanded lately. And things were really up in the air while that new manager was learning about the project.

Challenger: Can you think of something else?

Example 4: Examining Options and Alternatives

Depressed you: What else is left for me? My life is as good as over! The only thing left for me to do is to die. I'll probably mess that up, too.

Challenger: Are you saying that you have no other options?

Depressed you: None that I can think of or would want to try.

Challenger: Let's look at that, then. On the one hand, you say there are no options. On the other hand, you suggest that there are options that you have in mind that you dismiss because you don't want to try. I'd like to help you to look at the options, as limited as they seem. Let's see if you and I can generate at least one other possibility.

Depressed you: I haven't been going to therapy as regularly as I used to. Maybe I should start doing that again.

Challenger: Great! What might be another option?

Example 5: Decatastrophizing

In thinking about approaching someone:

Depressed you: She'll think I'm an idiot.

Challenger: And what if she does? What would be so horrible if she thinks you're an idiot? Does that make you one?

Depressed you: It *would* be awful.

Challenger: Let's try again. What if she does think something about you? First, how do you know what she's thinking? And second, is what she thinks true?

Depressed you: (Smiling) I can't easily answer either of those questions. Either way, it wouldn't destroy me, so it's not that terrible, but it still seems pretty bad.

Challenger: You're right, it may seem so. Now what?

Example 6: Examining Expected Consequences

Challenger: Close your eyes and picture what you think will happen in this situation.

Picture walking into the kitchen at home. Your parents are both there, and your father asks you about the exam.

What will he say or do?

Depressed you: He'll get furious when I tell him that I've failed. He'll yell at me and tell me for the millionth time that I am wasting his hard-earned money. He'll tell me that I might as well drop out of school.

Challenger: What are the chances that he will actually say that to you?

Depressed you: The chance of this happening is about 50%, but actually my first thought was that he would throw me out of the house and make me drop out of school. Chances are that he would probably tell me that I had been doing a lousy job and then carry on for days about how I need to apply myself.

Challenger: If he reacted this way, what would you do?

Depressed you: I would try to accept that he'd be angry for a while, and understand that eventually he'd calm down.

Example 7: Listing Advantages and Disadvantages

Depressed you: I can't stay in this marriage. If I stay, I'll die.

Challenger: From what you've described in the past, there are many parts to the relationship, both good and bad. Leaving has a lot of consequences. What are your other options?

Depressed you: I don't know.

Challenger: Let's explore the possibilities. We can work at making two lists. The first can be the advantages and the disadvantages of staying with Steve. The second can look at the advantages and disadvantages of leaving.

Depressed you: Aren't they the same?

Challenger: Not really. There will be some overlap, but the lists will show some very different ideas.

Example 8: Turning Adversity to Advantage

Depressed you: I lost my job. Now what do I do?

Challenger: With the job gone, what keeps you in food service? You've thought of other jobs; in fact, you've spoken of some new career directions. What about those?

Depressed you: That's true, maybe I don't have to worry. It could be freeing. I have hated that job. This could be a great opportunity to try something new.

Challenger: Let's explore that idea, look more actively at your options.

Example 9: Labeling Distortions

Depressed you: This always happens to *me*. Whenever *I'm* in a hurry, there's a traffic jam.

Challenger: What are you doing?

Depressed you: I'm personalizing.

Challenger: When you consider it further, do you really believe that the traffic jam had to do with you?

Depressed you: Well, of course not.

Example 10: Guided Association and Discovery

A 39-year-old single mother reported feeling depressed and suicidal after her boyfriend, who was an alcoholic, left her to date other women.

Depressed you: I kept demanding that we should have a relationship. I kept telling myself that I like him and that we should have a relationship. So why did he leave me for her? (pause) She must be better than I am.

Challenger: You think she's better than you are?

Depressed you: Yes. She is able to do what I can't.

Challenger: That seems very upsetting, to think that she can do what you can't. What does that mean to you, exactly? *Why is it so upsetting to you?*

Depressed you: It means that I'm inadequate.

Challenger: Being inadequate *seems so terrible because it means what?*

Depressed you: That I can't ever have a relationship. That I'm not able to grow or change.

Challenger: And not growing or changing. *Why does that seem so bad?*

Depressed you: That I'll be lonely. I won't have anyone to share my life with.

Challenger: *And that would be terrible because?*

Depressed you: My daughter and I won't have a family. We'll be alone.

Challenger: And being alone *would be horrible because?*

Depressed you: It makes me worry that she'll be an orphan if something bad happens to me. There will be nobody there for her.

Challenger: So, you've mentioned that she's better than you are, you feel that you're inadequate and aren't growing or changing, and you worry that there won't be anyone there for you or your daughter. Right?

Depressed you: Yes. . . .

Challenger: Do you see any connections here? Any common themes among all these thoughts?

Depressed you: Well, I seem to feel that having a family, a man, is very important. I feel inadequate . . . that I need the relationship to be OK.

Challenger: That's what you believe you need to feel secure? To feel happy?

Depressed you: Yes.

Challenger: Does that seem typical of you? The way you usually view things?

Example 11: Using Paradox or Exaggeration

Depressed you: No one has ever helped me, no one cares.

Challenger: No one? No one in the whole world has ever, in any small way, offered you any help at all?

Depressed you: That's going too far. Of course people have helped me . . . but not when I needed them.

Challenger: Let's look at that. It changes the issue a bit. People have helped, but not when you wanted or needed them to help. Are there ways that you could get more help by asking differently or by asking different people?

Example 12: Scaling

Challenger: If you put your sadness of a scale of 1 to 100, how sad are you right now?

Depressed you: 90 to 95.

Challenger: That's pretty high. Can you think of the saddest you've ever been in your life? When was that?

Depressed you: When my mother died.

Challenger: How sad were you then?

Depressed you: 100!

Challenger: Can you remember a time that you were the happiest you have ever been?

Depressed you: Yes, the day I graduated from college. I was so proud of myself!

Challenger: If that was a happy time, label that 1 for "not sad". Use those two events, your college graduation as "1" for "not sad" and your mom's death as "100" for "extremely sad". Compared with those events, how sad are you now?

Depressed you: Well, compared with that, this is a 50, maybe 45.

Example 13: Replacement Imagery

Susan had trouble resisting sweets when she felt depressed.

Challenger: Imagine you are sitting at the table with a piece of apple pie in front of you.

Depressed you: OK. I can picture it. It looks so good!

Challenger: Now, imagine that you pick up your fork and lift a bite of the pie to your mouth, only to find that the pie is stale and hard.

Depressed you: Yuk! I can't eat it.

Challenger: Next, imagine picking up the piece of pie and throwing it in the trash can.

Example 14: Cognitive Rehearsal

Challenger: Close your eyes and picture speaking with your girlfriend. Can you picture that?

Depressed you: Yes. I don't like what I'm seeing.

Challenger: What do you see? Describe it.

Depressed you: I see her listening to me and then turning away. I start begging her to stay and then I feel embarrassed and humiliated.

Challenger: Can you picture not begging? Let's try to construct a picture you can live with, both literally and figuratively. What would be in the scene you would like to see happen?

Example 15: Self-Instruction or Coaching

Challenger: How can you deal more effectively with your son Jon when he starts to misbehave?

Depressed you: I just automatically respond. I need some space. I want to tell him to get out.

Challenger: What would happen if you could tell yourself that you don't have to respond immediately? You need to just walk away so you won't say something you will regret.

Depressed you: Well, if I listened to myself, I would probably be in far better shape.

Challenger: That's interesting! If you could tell yourself directly that it would be better to leave the situation, both you and Jon would do better. Is that so?

Depressed you: I suppose. But how can I talk to myself rationally when I'm so angry?

Challenger: Let's practice.

Example 16: Thought Stopping

Depressed you: I keep thinking about causing the plane to crash. I'm sweating just thinking about it. I'm really getting upset. . . .

Challenger: *Stop!* When you start having these thoughts, it's really important to stop before you lose control. What just happened? What helped you to stop?

Depressed you: The noise, I guess.

Example 17: Focusing

Challenger: Take a couple of deep breaths and repeat to yourself the word *one*. Whenever another depressive or anxious thought comes to your mind, just say to yourself again, "one."

Depressed you: This feels silly.

Challenger: I know. We want to see if you can interfere with the racing negative thoughts you described.

Depressed you: One . . . one. This is probably not going to work. How will I know when 10 minutes have gone by? I'm not doing this right. One (eyes still closed).

Depressed you: (After 10 minutes) I do feel somewhat better. The negative thoughts seemed to go away a little bit.

References

Beck, A. T. (1967). *Depression: Clinical, experimental, and theoretical aspects.* New York: Hoeber Medical Division, Harper & Row.

Beck, A. T. (1976). *Cognitive therapy and the emotional disorders.* New York: International Universities Press.

Beck, A. T. (1983). Cognitive therapy of depression: New perspectives. In P. J. Clayton & J. E. Barrett (Eds.), *Treatment of depression: Old controversies and new approaches* (pp. 265–290). New York: Raven Press.

Beck, A. T., & Freeman, A. (1990). *Cognitive therapy of personality disorders.* New York: Guilford Press.

Beck, A. T., Rush, A. J., Shaw, B. F., & Emery, G. (1979). *Cognitive therapy of depression.* New York: Guilford Press.

Burns, D. D. (1980). *Feeling good: the new mood therapy.* New York: Morrow.

Clark, D. M., Fairburn, C. G., & Gelder, M. G. (1997). *Science and practice of cognitive behaviour therapy.* New York: Oxford University Press.

Dobson, K. S. (1989). A meta-analysis of the efficacy of cognitive therapy for depression. *Journal of Consulting and Clinical Psychology, 57,* 414–419.

Ellis, A. (1973). *Humanistic psychotherapy: The rational-emotive approach.* New York: Julian Press.

Ellis, A., & Harper, R.A. (1961). *A guide to rational living.* Englewood Cliffs, NJ: Prentice-Hall.

Ellis, A., & Harper, R. A. (1975). *A new guide to rational living.* North Hollywood, CA: Wilshire Book.

Freud, S. (1991). Mourning and melancholia. In J. Strachey (Ed. and Trans.), *The standard edition of the complete psychological works of Sigmund Freud* (Vol. 14, pp. 243–258). London: Hogarth Press. (Original work published 1917)

Gilson, M. L. (1984). Depression as measured by perceptual bias in binocular rivalry. *Dissertation Abstracts International, 44*(08), 2555B. (University Microfilms No. DA83-27351)

Lazarus, A. A. (1976). *Multimodal behavior therapy.* New York: Springer.

Meichenbaum, D., & Turk, D. C. (1987). *Facilitating treatment adherence: A practitioner's guidebook.* New York: Plenum Press.

National Institutes of Health. (1997). *Helpful facts about depressive illnesses* [NIH Publication No. 97-3875]. Rockville, MD: National Institute of Mental Health.

Piaget, J. (1966). *The origins of intelligence in children.* New York: International Universities Press.

Powell, M., & Hemsley, D.R. (1984). Depression: A breakdown of perpetual defence? *British Journal of Psychiatry,* 145, 358–362.

Seeger, P., & Blood, P. (Eds.) (1997). *Where have all the flowers gone: A musical autobiography.* Bethlehem, PA: Sing Out.

Seligman, M. E. P. (1991). *Learned optimism.* New York: A. A. Knopf.

Wright, J. H. (1987). Cognitive therapy and medication as combined treatment. In A. Freeman & V. B. Greenwood (Eds.), *Cognitive therapy: Applications in psychiatric and medical settings* (pp. 36–50). New York: Human Sciences Press.